ENGLISH PUBLIC HEALTH SERIES

Edited by SIR MALCOLM MORRIS, K.C.V.O.

HOUSING AND THE PUBLIC HEALTH

Housing and the Public Health

BY

JOHN ROBERTSON

C.M.G., O.B.E., M.D., B.Sc.

Medical Officer of Health of Birmingham

WITH 12 DIAGRAMS

CASSELL AND COMPANY, LTD
London, New York, Toronto and Melbourne

First published 1919

PREFACE

MY official life has brought me into intimate contact with the bad conditions under which the humbler classes in our towns have to exist and the remedies which may be applied to these conditions.

The experience thus gained enables me to assert with confidence that all these people (except perhaps a negligible minority) will respond to improved conditions, provided that the change is adequate. We may in this sense "trust the people."

No single condition in the lives of the masses has such a damaging effect on health, or does harm in so many other ways, as bad housing. It is for this reason that I feel strongly the need of raising the standard of "housing," so that every human life may enjoy the advantages of a healthy house in healthy surroundings. My minimal standard may be considered high, but I do not think that any substantial reduction could be made without risking the return of some of the unwholesome conditions we wish to remedy.

The opinions expressed result from my own experience; I have therefore given but few refer-

Preface

ences. The following special Reports, however, from the second of which, commonly known as the Tudor Walters Report, I have been allowed to reproduce illustrations, will be found valuable :

Report of the Royal Commission on Housing for Scotland (Cd. 8731).

Report to the Local Government Board on questions of Building Construction in connection with the provision of Dwellings for the Working Classes in England and Wales (Cd. 9191).

I have appended to the text a list of works of reference and other documents which are essential for anyone desiring to follow up the subject.

J. R.

CONTENTS

INTRODUCTION

CHAPTER I

The Influence of Bad Housing on the Health of the People

CHAPTER II

The Structural Requirements of a Healthy Dwelling

Contents

ix

Contents

LIST OF DIAGRAMS

xi

Housing and Public Health

of the effects which were going to follow. May we not even to-day have precisely similar problems coming up for decision—problems in which the future has to be outlined, and that future is extraordinarily dim ? Who, for instance, is prepared to predict what will be even approximately the effects of any great development of aviation ? Yet it is conceivable that such a development may profoundly influence questions of housing, as well as other problems. It is unwise and ungenerous, then, to blame the distant past for what we have around us to-day. Rather is it important for us to recognise what is bad, and to use our every effort to remedy it as soon as possible.

Bearing in mind that what we suffer from in bad housing is the result of want of foresight or knowledge, it is peculiarly necessary, in attempting to put forward a policy, to satisfy ourselves that it is not a retrograde policy, and it behoves us to use every means in our power to ensure that we advocate at least the minimal requirements of healthy human life.

One of the perfectly marvellous facts

Introduction

which emerge from a study of human life is its capacity for adapting itself to extraordinarily adverse conditions. But for this adaptability many of the families which live in the crowded parts of our slums would have been exterminated long ago. Human life is able to adapt itself even to the adverse conditions of the Arctic and Antarctic zones and of the tropics ; but it is doubtful whether either of these extremes does as much damage to human life as is produced by bad housing, and all that is associated with it, in our towns.

We have, unfortunately, only imperfect methods of measuring the harm done by such influences as bad housing. The death-rate is a crude foot-rule, the sickness-rate is so incomplete as to be unusable in most cases, anthropometrical measurements are not much better, criminal statistics are not very direct in their bearing on the question, life-tables have yet to be worked out to show that slum-dwellers live under extraordinary handicaps, and nearly every other criterion is liable to such variation as to be of very limited value. But while this is so,

Housing and Public Health

there is such a mass of evidence already accumulated of the evil results of life under unwholesome conditions that no one will attempt to refute it.

The figures which are given in the first chapter indicate that, approximately, the death-rate in the slum areas of our towns is nearly twice as high as that in average artisan areas. It is, of course, not claimed for a single moment that the whole of this excess is due to the structure of the houses, but throughout this book the term "housing" is used in its widest sense as meaning all the influences which congregate round a house. The harm is even greater than is indicated by the figures. If it were possible to reduce the average death-rate in this country to the very moderate figure of 10 deaths per 1,000 people living, we should save more than 200,000 lives every year, and at least ten times this number of cases of illness. The money value of this would be enormous, yet it is well within the range of accomplishment in a generation or two if an earnest attempt be made. And largely this attempt must take the form of pro-

4

Introduction

viding wholesome conditions for those who are now living in unwholesome surroundings.

If you take the employee who works in a dusty, ill-lighted factory all day and lives and sleeps in an ill-ventilated, ill-lighted, and perhaps damp house, and is ignorant of the kinds of food he ought to buy, it is almost certain that you will get in him and his family a high incidence of disease. The rural labourer, too, who because of his poor pay has poor food, with long hours of work, and often has to pass his nights in a damp, ill-ventilated or unventilated sleeping-room, is marked out for ill-health, disease, inefficiency in his work, and early death.

To a very considerable extent there is absolute agreement as to the minimal standard required for a dwelling-house so far as accommodation, arrangement, and structure are concerned, but it is only within very recent years that it has been realised that something more than well-planned bricks and mortar is required. It is only a few years ago that the value of town planning was first emphasised as one of the essential adjuncts to reasonably good hous-

Housing and Public Health

ing. Scarcely any great social problem has been more earnestly considered than this, and there is perhaps none in which more progress has been made in so short a time. In considering housing from a Public Health point of view, too much emphasis cannot be laid on the fact that bad housing is but one component of a vicious circle of which the other components are drink, poverty, vice, dirtiness, carelessness, and ignorance. And bad housing, to change the metaphor, is the link of the chain which may most easily, and with the most permanent benefits, be broken. This, therefore, is the most important of all the links for the social reformer to deal with.

But why has there been so much delay in grappling with a problem which is of such vital importance to the nation? The answer is to be found in the many and difficult economic questions which enter into it. A full description of all these questions would be out of place in a little book on the health aspects of housing, but it is obvious that without reference to these a very important side of the problem would be ignored.

Introduction

Ten years ago it was the custom to pay navvies, railway surface men, and many classes of labourers in our provincial towns from eighteen to twenty-two shillings a week. On these wages a man married and brought up a family—often a large family. These people were reliable, hard-working, thrifty, and clean. They had to settle for themselves the rent they could afford. In the country it varied from 2s. to 4s. per week, and in the towns it was a little more. For these rents they got the best value in houses which could be given, but the houses were the derelicts of the district, or houses which would not have been occupied but for the stress of poverty. No wonder that these labourers often looked with envy at the good buildings which were provided for the horses and cows of those who recognised that good housing was essential to healthy animal life.

Largely, then, the bad housing of to-day is due to the fact that people have been unable to pay for wholesome houses with wholesome surroundings, and when we consider the future it must be from the point

7

Housing and Public Health

of view that never again must the labourer be allowed to suit the house to his wage, but rather the house must be suited to the minimal requirements of human life, and we must see to it that the wage is so raised that these requirements may be fulfilled.

If there is one thing more important than another in housing, it is that human life demands at least a minimum standard of accommodation, of quality, and of environment. An attempt is made in these pages to set out those standards. If rents are to be economic, as it is desirable they should be, it is obvious that the housing question will turn very largely upon the wages question.

In erecting standards to-day we must be careful not to repeat the mistake made by our forefathers seventy years ago in setting the standards too low. Nay, more—it is for us to consider, in the light of the knowledge and experience we have acquired, whether it would not be wiser to provide something above the minimum for even the humblest of those around us.

ferring them to better conditions; but such an immediate transference never takes place in practice. We have seen the value of great changes as we have watched the results of the introduction of a water-carriage system. Within a few years people who had never had the chance of using the water-closet have become educated into using it properly, and appreciate the change from the old condition of a stinking privy midden to the modern water-carriage system.

For many years every obstacle was put in the way of providing the working classes with the water-carriage system. But in most towns it has now been introduced, with results which have been astonishingly good. In Birmingham, for example, the cases of enteric fever have fallen in number during the past fifteen years from approximately 800 per annum to approximately 20 per annum, largely as a result of removing the revoltingly filthy conditions which the people formerly had to endure.

This is only one of many similar illustrations of the direct value of better conditions, and of the readiness of the people to appreciate them.

If one takes the older portion of any large city it will be found that the mortality-rate is high, and that it has been continuously high for half a century. If in these same towns you look at the more recently built portions, where the great

Housing and Public Health

bulk of the skilled artisans live, you will find that in them the mortality-rate is low. Yet not many years ago these same better-class artisans would have lived in the districts where now the high death-rate rules and where the death-rate has always been high. That is to say, the change in their death-rate is largely due to their better housing and other conditions.

Bad housing, while mainly limited to the poorer parts of our towns, is not without influence on other groups of the community. There is probably no medical man who could not mention groups of cases of tuberculosis largely due to residence in good-class houses where the lighting and free supply of fresh air are so defective as to predispose to the disease.

Much statistical information is available in every town to show that where families live under bad housing conditions, there the general mortality is high, and sickness is so frequent as to involve a large expenditure.

In Glasgow it is a custom for the poor to live in one- or two-roomed houses in tenement buildings. Somewhat over 60 per cent. of the whole population live under such conditions. Dr. Chalmers, the Medical Officer of Health of the city, has reported that the mortality-rates in these houses as compared with larger houses were as follows :

Bad Housing

				Death-rate
One-roomed houses	.	.	.	. 25·9 per 1,000
Two-roomed houses	.	.	.	. 16·5 ,, ,,
Three-roomed houses	.	.	.	. 11·5 ,, ,,
Four-roomed houses	.	.	.	. 10·8 ,, ,,

That is to say, the one-roomed houses, with a population of 104,000 persons (a population equal to that of the whole of Halifax or Wolverhampton), had a death-rate more than double that of three-roomed houses, with a population of 160,000 persons.

Unhealthy areas.—If, instead of individual houses, one takes whole areas and compares these with other areas, one gets similar remarkable differences. In the first group of figures that follow are set out the results obtained in two Birmingham areas; one mostly a poor area with the worst dwellings and the worst environment, and the other a fair-class artisan area with moderately good houses, though not sufficiently good. It will be noted that, compared with the fair-class area, the death-rate in the bad area is nearly double, and the infant-mortality rate double; that the death-rate from tuberculosis is very much higher, from measles nearly three times as high, and from diarrhœa and enteritis nearly four times as high. Similar figures are given for areas in Liverpool, Manchester, London, and Aberdeen.

13

Housing and Public Health

	Rubishaw		Greyfriars
Population	20,210	..	13,850
Death-rate	10·2	..	16·3
Birth-rate	16·2	..	34·1
Infant-mortality rate . .	83	..	170
Excess of births over deaths .	6·0	..	17·8
Death-rate per 1,000 :—			
Zymotic disease . . .	0·8	..	3·1
Pulmonary tuberculosis .	0·6	..	1·3
Other forms of tuberculosis .	0·2	..	0·7

In considering these groups of figures for unhealthy areas, it is well to bear in mind that they would have been worse but for the fact that every year, even into the slummiest areas of our towns, there is a considerable migration of healthy country stock, which, being more resistant to disease than is the slum-dweller, prevents the figures from mounting so high as they would otherwise have done.

Many attempts have been made to estimate the total loss of life to be ascribed to unwholesome areas, and figures have been frequently obtained which stagger the imagination. It is, for instance, computed that in the unwholesome areas of London and the county boroughs of England there is, in the twenty millions of people living in these towns, an annual loss of 50,000 lives which ought not to occur—a loss over and above the average mortality in the ordinary

Bad Housing

artisan areas. It has already been pointed out that with a death-rate of 10 per 1,000—a death-rate which ought to be easily attainable—over 200,000 lives per annum would be saved.

Army rejects and unwholesome conditions of life. — Many other illustrations could be given of the harm resulting from unwholesome conditions of life. Perhaps the best is that of the recruiting officer during the War. The figures are misleading and inaccurate in certain details, but the general conclusions are valuable. It has been said, probably correctly, that something under 40 per cent. of the adult population could be classed as A1 in the grouping for Army purposes.

We must bear in mind, however, that many of the men rejected for the Army are perfectly sound and wholesome lives for civilian purposes. For example, a man who was rejected because of a rupture, or defective vision, or varicose veins, or any other of a hundred minor ailments, would be classed as a healthy life from the civil point of view, so that the figure of 40 per cent. is misleading. While this is so, however, there can be no question that the defective physique and stamina of a large number of these rejects was due to the unwholesome conditions under which they had lived and worked. No one who was constantly seeing the troops in training could fail to be im-

number of people occupying it, so as to prevent overcrowding.

6. It should have adequate sunlight and efficient ventilation.
7. The internal arrangements should be such as to lessen house work.
8. It should have a sufficient water supply, and in the case of town houses this should be laid on inside.
9. It should be provided with a bath.

(b) The environment

1. The house and garden or yard should be self-contained.
2. The area allotted to each dwelling must be sufficient to permit of free circulation of air and direct access of sunlight.
3. Either inside the dwelling or immediately adjoining outside there must be a water-closet, together with adequate drainage arrangements to carry off all liquid organic matter.
4. Provision must be made for the storage and frequent removal of solid refuse.
5. Facilities must be provided for the home washing and drying of clothes.
6. Provision must be made to prevent soakage of filth into the ground in the immediate vicinity of the house.

Structural Requirements

(c) General provisions

1. The house should have good general amenity in its surroundings.
2. The area in which it is erected should be free from soot or grit in the air, or effluvium, or noise, or nuisances from factories.
3. There should be in the immediate neighbourhood sufficient transport facilities.
4. Provision is necessary for the recreation of the occupants in the open air, and for institutes.
5. Provision should be made for gardens, allotments, etc., and for the general beautifying of the environment by tree planting, etc.

We may now embark upon the subject proper of the present chapter, viz. the structural requirements of a healthy dwelling.

Protection from the weather.— The fact that a house is not weather-proof appeals, perhaps, to the uninitiated more than any other feature as the one which makes a house uninhabitable. It must not, however, be overlooked that all of us can stand exposure to weather to a quite remarkable degree. Barely thirty years ago it was the custom to advise that a delicate lady who was suffering

Housing and Public Health

from early pulmonary tuberculosis should be kept in a room with a fire burning both day and night, and with sandbags placed at the window and door to keep out draught. Such a patient generally went from bad to worse and died. To-day, for a tuberculous patient, a bed in the open air, with protection merely from the rain and the worst of the wind, is the treatment in vogue. No fire is provided, but heat is given by hot-water bottles, and the moving air is allowed to play freely all round. The effect of the "weather," under such conditions, is often wonderful in reducing cough, bringing down the temperature, doing away with night sweats, increasing the appetite, and improving the patient's sense of well-being. The two essentials for such a delicate person exposed to moving air are sufficiency of nourishing food and adequate clothing.

Again, open-air schools demonstrate the harmlessness of the "weather," if there is a minimum of protection and the food and clothing are good and sufficient. The exposure of our soldiers to inclement weather further demonstrates the fact that free air supply and even low temperatures do not of themselves cause illness, but rather that this free exposure to atmospheric influences is stimulating and health-giving.

One must be careful, therefore, in condemning a dwelling as unwholesome because it is not

Structural Requirements

weather-proof; but in nearly all cases a house that is so dilapidated as not to be weather-proof is insanitary in other respects. And if such a house is occupied by people who are underfed and underclad, exposure to the weather undoubtedly has ill effects, for the occupants are liable to contract infection from the many germs which flourish there. Moreover, while exposure to the weather is under certain conditions wholesome rather than the reverse, it is essential that for family life the house should be free from draughts and impervious to rain, so that the ordinary work of the family, such, for instance, as the bathing of the baby and other purely domestic operations, may go on without danger or discomfort. Access of weather must therefore be under control.

Protection against extremes of temperature.— Many dwelling-houses are so badly constructed as to be excessively hot in summer and excessively cold in winter. Nobody who has lived in a galvanised iron hut during hot weather and during cold weather can have failed to notice the difference between such a structure and a house with thick walls and a substantial roof. Two groups of people are definitely influenced by excessive heat inside a dwelling-house in summer time — infants and invalids.

Many of our present slum-dwellings have been erected without any regard to protection against

Housing and Public Health

extremes of temperature. Particularly is this the case in the back-to-back houses which face south, and in single-roomed houses and tenements. If the walls and roofs of such houses are thin and badly constructed, it is not infrequent to find the maximum temperature inside the living-room running up to over 90 degrees Fahr. At such a temperature infants and invalids are apt to suffer in various ways. It is alleged by several German investigators that many of the deaths which we attribute to epidemic summer diarrhœa are really due to heat-stroke (Hitzslag). No one who has had charge of an infant can have failed to become aware of the distress it suffers in a room which is too warm, and every one who has had charge of invalids is aware of the more rapid progress to recovery made in winter as compared with summer. For years it has been the rule in many sanatoria to place patients in the shade in the summer, so as to keep them out of the heat, because it is well recognised that their progress, when exposed to heat, is so much slower.

Too little attention has been paid in the past to the structure of the dwelling-house in regard to its capability of keeping out heat in summer and cold in winter. The upper storeys of cottages have frequently been built of 4½-in. walls, and the roof is correspondingly slight, with the result that in summer the bedrooms are unbearably hot, and

Structural Requirements

the dwellers undoubtedly have lowered vitality from occupying these rooms. Many attics, even in well-built houses, are so hot in summer and so cold in winter as to be extremely uncomfortable. It will be shown in a later chapter how much can be done to prevent the passage of heat through the walls of dwelling-houses.

Dampness.—This is one of the most important of the conditions which make a house unwholesome. In its worst aspects it is due to defective construction during the period of industrial development, when porous bricks were used without a damp-course, and floors were laid with porous tiles without any concrete below. Such a house is not only damp but, because it is damp, is cold and chilly. Dampness rises from the ground through most building materials by reason of capillarity, and such dampness will usually rise in brick walls well into the bedroom storey.

Experiments made with bricks from forty-four different sources showed that such bricks, on an average, take up 18 per cent. of their weight in water. Similarly, the porous tile which is generally used for kitchen floors absorbs 18 per cent. of its weight in water. Bricks taken from the walls of damp houses show that 15 per cent. of moisture is retained. It is therefore obvious that a brick wall may be condemned either because it is built

Housing and Public Health

of porous bricks and is exposed during wet weather, or because no damp-course has been provided.

Any impervious material may be used as a damp-course, so long as the material is one that will not disintegrate in course of time. Probably a lead damp-course, the one used by the ancients, is best of all. Various bituminous compositions are now used, with very good results. But such a damp-course will not protect a wall from dampness if the material of which the wall is composed is porous, and therefore in practice it is important to secure that the materials of which a wall is built are not highly porous. In an area where grit stone is prevalent there are to be found stones which would otherwise make excellent building material but which are so porous that when rain is driven by wind against a wall built of such stone the water runs through considerable thicknesses of the wall and trickles down inside the building in pools.

This, of course, is a very exceptional condition; but between such stones as that described and an almost impervious material there are all gradations. Ordinary building bricks are seldom sufficiently impervious when built as a 9-in. wall to keep the wall dry, and thus, in a very large number of the houses built of 9-in. brickwork, the walls are either damp continuously, or are damp under special weather conditions. In all new buildings, therefore, some form of protection, such as the inter-

Structural Requirements

vention of a cavity, should be provided against dampness from this source. Two 4½-in. walls tied together will answer the purpose. Similarly, in most instances a 14-in. brick wall is sufficient.

Another common method of obviating dampness is to rough-cast or cement the brickwork on the outside. The practical point to bear in mind is that for a really dry dwelling for the poorer classes a 9-in. brick wall is not of itself sufficient.

A defect, comparatively little understood, due to damp walls, is that mortar covering the inside of such walls undergoes a chemical change of probably a very complicated nature, causing the formation of hydroscopic lime salts; hence the common opinion of builders that once a wall becomes damp it will always be damp. In such a case, the mortar should be taken off and the wall rough-cast on the outside; fresh plaster put on the inside will not then draw damp. It is important to remember this in repairing buildings which from any cause have become damp.

Perhaps the most mischievous form of dampness is that arising from the fact that in many old dwellings the floor of the living-room is of tiles or stones laid on the damp soil. Evaporation from such a floor into the living-room is constantly going on, and it is impossible therefore to keep the living-room warm. There can be no doubt that such a condition lowers vitality. It is not sufficient to lay these stones or tiles on a thin layer of sand or ashes. The only sufficient protection is a layer of cement concrete under the tiles of the floor. It is a common occurrence to find in houses with damp floors that it is difficult to get the kitchen floor dry after it has been washed. This is due to the excess of moisture in the tiles. The provision of a cellar under the kitchen floor is advocated as a means of preventing dampness; but unless the floor is well constructed dampness will still travel laterally by porosity just as easily as it travels vertically.

Capacity for being kept clean.—The floors, walls, and woodwork generally should be smooth and capable of being washed or brushed or dusted. It is not uncommon for floors, especially tiled living-room floors, to be so uneven and broken from the chopping of sticks that it is quite impossible to clean them. Similarly, walls which are cracked or which have the plaster knocked off cannot be properly cleaned. Loose and defective woodwork allows large accumulations of dust, and in this respect skirting boards and all matchboarding are an abomination; they harbour not only dust, but all that dust means.

During the great industrial development of this country the bedroom floors in many areas were laid with boards which were not tongued and grooved, with the result that in the course of many

Structural Requirements

years large quantities of dust have accumulated underneath the floor boards and on the top of the living-room ceiling. Frequently as much as an inch of dust is found to have passed through the floor in these circumstances, and it is possible to hatch out fleas and to grow a great variety of micro-organisms from such dust. In one instance dust from underneath a floor was administered to guinea-pigs, which developed tuberculosis. A house with dust under the floors and woodwork smells stuffy, and although such dust is not often blown back into the dwelling-room, there is no doubt that at times this happens. Possibly this may be the cause of illnesses the origin of which cannot be accounted for on ordinary grounds.

One of the reasons, therefore, for the high sickness-rate in slum areas is the inability to keep dilapidated houses clean, even if the people themselves have a taste for cleanliness. The infectious nature of the dust has often been proved, particularly in the case of tuberculosis. Cornet and others have taken samples of dust from mantelshelves, picture-rails, and other parts of rooms which have been inhabited by careless consumptives, and the giving of such dust to guinea-pigs has transmitted the disease to them. Such investigations have been repeated on several occasions in this country, and it may be taken as indisputable that all ledges where dust can settle should be avoided.

Housing and Public Health

The custom of building dwellings without plastering the interior, and thus leaving rough surfaces, is much to be deprecated. Such a wall can never be kept clean, and if the rough surface of the brick is left it catches and retains dust, and the place becomes unwholesome. Unfortunately, not only houses but many schools have been erected with these rough brick walls.

Overcrowding.—When the subject of bad housing is discussed, overcrowding is usually the condition which appeals most to those who desire that better accommodation should be provided. It must, however, be clearly understood that overcrowding is seldom more than relative, and it is therefore very difficult to formulate standards for the number of houses which may be erected on any given area, or for the number of individuals who may occupy any dwelling-house, if really effective precautions are taken thoroughly to ventilate the parts occupied.

The accompanying little plan (Fig. 1) of a very crowded area in Birmingham contains houses at the rate of 16 per acre, and a population at the rate of 61 per acre. Yet both of these figures come well within the limits of our housing and town-planning schemes. The fact is that the area in question is overcrowded by being occupied not only with dwellings but with works of various kinds.

It is possible, of course, so to arrange the ven-

Structural Requirements

tilation of a dwelling as to enable large numbers of persons to occupy and sleep in the house without

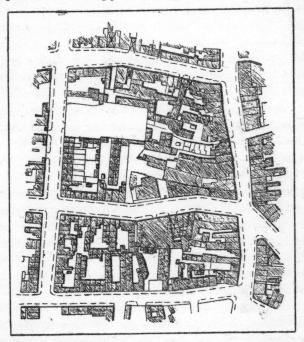

Fig. 1.—Area in Birmingham crowded with dwellings and factories.
(*From the Ordnance Survey.*)

detriment to health. But while this is so, there is nothing which does more harm to the community than overcrowding, be it overcrowding on space or overcrowding in rooms.

Housing and Public Health

Let us first consider the overcrowding of a dwelling. The old idea was that the products of respiration accumulated to such an extent in an occupied room as slowly to poison the occupants. We now know that the real causes of the damage done by overcrowding are (1) the stagnation of air, and (2) the spread of infection due to the proximity of the inmates to one another. In an ordinary cottage a small ventilator in the pantry or scullery is sufficient in nearly all cases to keep the respiratory carbonic acid in the bedrooms down to a reasonable limit, but nothing short of the open window and open chimney will enable a sufficient amount of moving air to pass across the rooms. Prof. Leonard Hill, in his Report to the Local Government Board on Ventilation, in July, 1914, has brought together a large amount of evidence to demonstrate the need for the ventilation of rooms to be so good as to cause the air to be in continuous motion. The bracing effect of a walk on a windy day is largely due to the movement of the air. Similarly, the sound sleep, and the feeling of freshness resulting from sleep, in a well-ventilated room are largely due to movement of the air.

One of the features of a slum area is the number of dwellers who are afraid of opening a window, and particularly a bedroom window. In part this is due to ignorance, but mainly it is due to insufficient food and insufficient bedclothing. During recent years observations have been made of the number of bedroom windows open in houses of different rentals. These observations were generally made in spring and summer, and they showed that the number of open bedroom windows was in proportion to the rental. In the poorest areas during the heat of summer less than 10 per cent. of the bedroom windows were open, and in winter less than 2 per cent.

Spray infection.—The greatest harm done by overcrowding is that due to spray infection from the mouth or nose. For many years it has been said that tuberculosis runs in families. The real explanation is that spray infection from one case infects the other members of the family. It is a question not of heredity but of infection. We now know that many diseases are spread by spray infection from the mouth or nose of an infected to a susceptible person during coughing, sneezing, or loud talking.

No more convincing demonstration of this could have been given than the evidence obtained among the troops during the War. So long ago as 1861 a Royal Commission laid down as the standard for soldiers in barracks in peace time 60 sq. ft. of floor space per man, and 600 cub. ft. of air space. This floor space is reduced to 40 sq. ft. in war time. In the barracks or huts which served our soldiers during the War it has been found that with ade-

Housing and Public Health

quate ventilation—and this in winter necessitates a sufficient supply of blankets — the men have remained uniformly healthy, even under bad weather conditions. On the other hand, it has been found with a regularity which is remarkable that any reduction of the floor space below 40 sq. ft. per man is sooner or later followed by outbreaks of disease, such as coryza, measles, cerebro-spinal fever, sore throat, and other ailments that are conveyed by spray infection.

The temporary huts erected during the War were of two sizes—20 ft. wide and 15 ft. wide. The narrower hut allowed 5 ft. 6 in. between the mouths of adjacent soldiers, while the wider hut allowed only 4 ft. 4 in. In every instance the narrow hut scored when the conditions were comparable. Similarly, in transports and in merchant ships the placing of hammocks close to one another has been followed by disastrous outbreaks of the diseases spread by spray infection.

There can be little doubt, therefore, that one of the most serious results of overcrowding is infection by reason of proximity of the dwellers to one another. It is probable that an interval of at least 4 ft. 6 in. should be maintained.

Certain other standards as to overcrowding have existed for many years. The Registrar-General has assumed that a house is overcrowded if occupied on an average by more than two per-

Structural Requirements

sons per inhabited room. Based on this standard, the twelve largest towns in England showed overcrowding in varying degrees, from 43 per 1,000 in excess in Nottingham to 316 per 1,000 in excess in Newcastle, the excess figure for London being 177, for Birmingham 100, for Liverpool 101, for Manchester 72, and for Leeds 112. In the main this standard is useful, but obviously it is open to criticism, for it does not take into consideration the size of the rooms or the use made of them. It is, for instance, not at all infrequent to find slum-dwellers huddling together in one bedroom and leaving one or two other bedrooms unoccupied because of lack of furniture or bedclothes.

Another standard of overcrowding often used is that contained in the bye-laws regulating houses let in lodgings. It is usually 500 cub. ft. per adult and 250 cub. ft. per child under 10 years of age. The Royal Commission on Housing of the Industrial Population in Scotland, in their excellent Report (Cd. 8731), recommended that these figures should be fixed as a standard for general adoption in cottage property. If one assumes that a bedroom is 8 ft. high, this would require 62½ sq. ft. of floor space per adult, a figure which closely approximates to that which has been found during the past half century to be a sufficient standard for barracks.

Overcrowding on space.—By this is meant the

35

number of houses per acre of land. It is now
generally recognised by the best authorities that
there ought not to be more than 12 houses to
the gross acre. In many working-class residential areas, built on the best models, the number
is considerably less. If 12 houses per acre is
taken as a minimum and 4½ persons are allowed
for each house, we have 54 persons per acre. In
the most congested area of Birmingham there are
100 persons per acre. In the artisan area already
mentioned there are 44 persons per acre, in the
bad area of Liverpool 144, and in that of Manchester 98. In the six largest towns the average
density at the 1911 Census was as follows :

London	.	.	.	60·4 persons per acre.
Glasgow	.	.	.	61·9 ,, ,,
Birmingham	.	.	.	19·3 ,, ,,
Liverpool	.	.	.	44·9 ,, ,,
Manchester	.	.	.	33·0 ,, ,,
Leeds	.	.	.	20·6 ,, ,,

In London the density at the last Census varied
from 169 at Southwark to 14.7 at Woolwich. In
Birmingham the variation at the Census was from
1.1 to 97.2. In the central districts of a town,
where tenements prevailed, the number was higher.

Any general statement of population in connection with acreage is apt to be somewhat misleading, because in many of the areas where the

36

Structural Requirements

population is not large the district is still over-crowded by reason of the presence of factories and other buildings. This is indeed a very important cause of overcrowding on space, because such buildings shut out light and air, they make the dwellings dirty by the soot and dust which they emit, and they render the houses less habitable by the noise occasioned by machinery, transport, and in other ways.

It has not been sufficiently recognised in the past that some of our most overcrowded areas, and indeed many cottages which are the most unwhole-some, are made so by the utilisation of every bit of spare space for factories, workshops, and commercial buildings of all kinds. One of the great advantages of town planning lies in the fact that it is possible now to prohibit such buildings, unless with the sanction of the local authority, in a town-planned area.

The more recent bye-laws in regard to new buildings provide a certain safeguard against over-crowding on space, because such bye-laws provide for at least 300 sq. ft. of yard space in the rear of a cottage, and require that the dwelling shall be built to face a road of definite width, the space in the rear and the road in front being governed by the height of the building.

In former days it was the custom, in order to erect the largest possible number of small houses

Housing and Public Health

in a particular area, to group them in courtyards or in narrow streets or back lanes, with the result that we have large masses of the poorest classes crowded together and using in common the space round the dwellings. To make matters worse, much of the space in the vicinity of the dwellings is occupied by smoky works. Thus there is to-day an urgent need for thinning out the buildings on many areas in the centres of towns.

To recapitulate, the real harm from overcrowding is due mainly to three conditions, viz. (1) lack of appreciation of the value of moving air by the tenant, (2) ignorance of the fact that infection is spread by spray from the nose and mouth, (3) the erection of dwellings and other buildings in too close proximity to one another.

Ventilation.—From what has already been said it will be apparent that a dwelling-house which cannot be abundantly flushed with moving air must be regarded as unwholesome. Usually the chimney in a room acts as an excellent ventilator, causing suction of air through the room, particularly if the window or door be open. In rooms where there is no chimney it is essential that there should be some special ventilator—an air-brick or a Sheringham valve—which should be situated in the wall opposite, or at least far removed from, the window. Many country cottages are very unwholesome because of the absence of win-

Structural Requirements

dows which open and of fireplaces with chimneys which ventilate.

The best test as to whether a room is sufficiently flushed with moving air is one of the simplest and most easily applied. It is only necessary to remain in the open air for a minute or two and then enter the room to be tested. It will be at once found that where there is no through current of air stuffiness, a disagreeable smell, is very noticeable. If the test be applied to an occupied bedroom in almost any house, unless the window and chimney have been kept open, one is sensible of an unmistakable odour. Medical men who are accustomed to enter the sleeping-rooms of the sick at unexpected times know how impure and offensive the air usually is; indeed, one—a famous surgeon—used regularly to carry a stick to ventilate such rooms by knocking out a pane of glass.

It is frequently said that back-to-back houses are very unwholesome because of lack of ventilation. This is true only to a very limited extent so far as internal ventilation is concerned, because with a window and fireplace most of the rooms in a back-to-back house can be almost as efficiently ventilated as the rooms in an ordinary house. The real disadvantage of back-to-back houses is the lack of air space round the dwelling and the impossibility of providing sanitary accommodation to

Housing and Public Health

make them self-contained. Usually they are left
to be occupied by the poorest members of the community. Such houses are often the dirtiest and
most dilapidated. Thus it is conditions other than
internal ventilation which make back-to-back
houses so extremely undesirable.

Lighting. —Inadequate lighting, next to insufficient air supply and dirtiness, is perhaps the
most injurious defect in a dwelling-house. Unfortunately, we have no easily applied test for
ascertaining the minimum of sunlight, direct or
indirect, compatible with health. That badly
lighted rooms, with their dullness and gloom, have
a prejudicial influence on the health of the occupants is beyond doubt. Such conditions cause a
lowering of resistance, and, therefore, increased
susceptibility to a large number of diseases. In
the back-to-back houses of Birmingham there is a
definitely higher incidence of disease and of death
in those in which the windows face due north,
than in those in which the windows face due
south. Five hundred of such houses were taken in
two groups, one looking north and the other looking south, for a period of five years. The number
of deaths in the houses looking north was 145; in
those looking south, 139.

Everybody is familiar with the evil effect of bad
lighting on the health of those who have to work
in basements, where there is no direct sunlight.

Structural Requirements

The condition of anæmia and ill-health which results is obvious. As a general rule, the workers in such premises frequently change into more healthy surroundings, and in this way the maximum amount of harm is avoided.

It may here be asked why coal miners are as a class relatively healthy. The reply is that the coal miner works in ventilated mines and with sterile materials — conditions very different from the germ-laden air of basements and ill-ventilated houses.

Apart from its stimulating influence on the human body, sunlight, by destroying germs, plays a very important part in purifying the particulate matter in the air. This can easily be demonstrated by planting germs upon some suitable nutritive material in dishes and then keeping some of the dishes in the light and others in the dark. The germs in those exposed to sunlight are rapidly killed, while those placed in the dark grow and multiply with great vigour. By means of the spectroscope it is possible to take sunlight and dissect it into its component parts, violet through yellow to red, just as in the rainbow. It is the violet rays, or rather the rays beyond the violet end of the spectrum—the ultra-violet rays—which are lethal to germs of all kinds, and are so stimulating to plant growth. It is for this reason that the morning sunlight is more valuable than the

Housing and Public Health

evening sunlight, both for plant growth and for purifying purposes.

Four causes may be mentioned which keep out the sunlight from poor-class dwellings: (1) The windows may face due north, or approximately due north; (2) they may be of insufficient size; (3) the light may be obstructed by unclean window panes or by curtains, or (4) by adjacent buildings. The effects of the lack of sunlight in living-rooms which face due north have already been mentioned.

Deficient window-size is, perhaps, more noticeable in the country than in the town. Many of our most elegant country cottages have small, low windows. Where the best conditions for health have to be provided, as in hospitals and sanatoria, care is now taken that the windows shall extend to, or nearly to, the ceiling, so as to obtain the maximum amount of light. The most recent bye-laws require for a new house that each room shall have a window, clear of obstruction, equal in area to one-tenth of the floor space of the room, and also that at least one-half of that window area shall be made to open. It is obvious that such a standard is not a very scientific one, because the effective lighting of a room will depend largely upon its shape; but on the whole, for dwelling-houses, the bye-law standard is a good and sufficient working basis. The really harmful window is, as already mentioned, that often met

Structural Requirements

with in country cottages, consisting of one or two small panes of glass, which are puttied in, and which give insufficient light and no ventilation.

Curtains.—Even where adequate window-area is provided, it is very common to find that much of the light is obstructed by curtains of various kinds. Largely, this provision of curtains is made to secure privacy within the dwelling. But in the designing of a house privacy should be secured at a less cost than that of shutting out sunlight, and this can be done by setting back the dwelling from the road and using low curtains.

Some tenants fear that the sun will damage their furniture and coloured articles, and they keep out sunlight for this reason. Others, in large towns, allow the windows to become so dirty that an appreciable amount of light is shut out. In these cases it is the tar and soot from smoke which cause the windows to become obscured. The tar forms a yellow coating on the glass, which acts almost as effectively in shutting out the valuable rays as does the red glass in a photographer's dark room.

Water supply.—It will be a surprise to many who are not familiar with the homes of the lower industrial classes to know that a considerable number of dwellings in most of our large towns have no inside water supply. In the year 1913 there were 43,000 dwelling-houses in Birmingham

Housing and Public Health

without such a water supply. Usually in these cases the supply is derived from a standpipe near to but outside the house. In the country there are, of course, but few labouring men's dwellings with an internal water supply. In the case of the town dwelling there is an undoubted necessity for a water supply inside, and a house without such a supply ought to be considered unfit for human habitation.

Those who are familiar with the domestic requirements of the poorer artisans in a town are unanimous in testifying that the absence of an internal water supply is one of the chief causes of dirtiness, often to a degree which produces ill-health. A water supply inside a dwelling means that there is, in addition, a sink and wastepipe, and with such a provision the minimum of cleanliness is provided for. Personal ablution can be carried out with relatively little inconvenience, and the washing of floors, clothes, etc., is easy, as compared with a house where every drop of water has to be carried in and every drop of slop water has to be carried out.

The question arises whether in the old dwelling-houses in our towns it is possible to provide a water supply and a sink in the only living-room of the house. Unless this is well done the walls are apt to become damp. So far as can be ascertained, such a provision, although objected to by

Structural Requirements

the authorities in many English towns, is the regular custom in Scotland and in Continental and American towns, where not only is there a sink in the kitchen, but in the better-class houses there is also a washing-basin, with hot and cold water, in every bedroom.

For practical purposes there exists no legal power of requiring a supply of water to be laid on inside a dwelling-house.

In the country the problem of supplying cottages with water takes quite a different form. In the vast majority of cottages it is impracticable to lay on an interior supply, and the first question which arises, therefore, is as to what should be considered a reasonably available supply, and, secondly, whether the supply is wholesome. Many decisions have been given in the law courts as to the distance which is to be considered reasonable between the cottage and the source of supply. Probably every case must be judged on its own merits. Where it is possible to supply water, say, within 50 yards, a well as far as 500 yards away might be considered unreasonably distant. Water at a greater distance than a quarter of a mile is too far away for hand carriage, and in such cases it is desirable that some provision be made for conveying it in a tank.

As to the wholesomeness of the supply, the best rule to be guided by is that no water should be

Housing and Public Health

used for domestic purposes which does not come from a well or spring or other source which in ordinary circumstances cannot be contaminated. Such a rule properly applied would do away with numerous wells in back yards and other places where they are liable to contamination. In many of these cases both chemical and bacteriological examination indicates that the water is of excellent quality, and yet from an inspection of the source it is clear that the water may become contaminated.

A further question arises in connection with water supplies, viz. that of quantity. In the Navy about four gallons per head per day is required for all purposes, including personal ablutions and the washing of clothes. In many country cottages this amount is exceeded by one or two gallons. Where water has to be carried long distances by hand, the tenant will naturally be very reluctant to use more than is absolutely necessary. In certain instances, carefully recorded, of artisans' dwellings in a town, the amounts used per head, irrespectively of age, were 7, 6, 8½, 10, 12, 4½, and 5½ pints per day. In towns where the artisan classes predominate the amount used for domestic purposes seldom exceeds twelve gallons per day per head, provided that waste is prevented. If twelve gallons per head per day were to be used in a country cottage where there were six in the household, this would mean no less than eighteen

Structural Requirements

journeys with two buckets each containing two gallons, or twelve journeys with three-gallon buckets. It is obvious, therefore, that the absence of an internal water supply seriously interferes with the adequate use of water for cleansing purposes.

Disease due to polluted water is fortunately nowadays as infrequent as it was formerly frequent. One might almost say that more harm now arises from dirtiness due to scarcity of water than from contaminated supplies.

Baths.—Few old cottages are provided with a bath. Indeed, baths in dwelling-houses are of very recent origin. It is equally true that our modern development of city life is also of recent origin, and that certain special provisions need to be made in order to keep the dwellers in crowded areas healthy.

One of the essentials in every dwelling is a bath, and where a water supply and a sewer are available there ought to be a fixed bath. All sorts of schemes have been attempted to make it possible to supply a bath without having a bathroom, and although it is certain that some of the make-shift baths are better than none at all, opinion is now fairly definite that a bathroom ought to be provided for every cottage. There is no reason whatever why this bathroom should not have, in addition, a lavatory basin and a water closet, and

47

Housing and Public Health

such a bathroom is much better on the bedroom floor than downstairs.

It may be asked whether such a separate bathroom is essential. One even hears statements as to the frequent misuse of the bath. But there ought never to be any hesitation in providing a bathroom. Occasionally it will be used for some other purpose by those who are ignorant and have never had the pleasure of a bath, but in a very few years these people come to regard the bathroom as something that is indispensable.

The really important reason for providing a bathroom is that, in its absence, the taking of a bath in the scullery or in the kitchen of an artisan's dwelling is surrounded by so many difficulties that the bath provided becomes more or less useless. Yet it is just among these people that the need for frequent bathing is greatest, and, as I have said, they are fast coming to regard baths as necessities. It would be a retrograde step, therefore, not to provide a bathroom in new cottages. There is a small but definite proportion of people who seldom, if ever, have the opportunity of washing more than their hands and faces. Occasionally these visit the public baths, while at other times they make shift with tubs, as did our forefathers. But public baths or cottage baths never can supply the needs of a community with a taste for cleanliness. Swimming-baths are of

Structural Requirements

little value from the point of view of cleansing the skin, because they are used as a means of recreation, and only during the few summer months.

In a very large proportion of small houses the bedrooms are so congested with furniture that there is no room even for a tub; nor are there reasonable facilities and privacy in the kitchen or scullery, and so these people go dirty. If this statement is doubted, it is only necessary to inquire of the casualty nurse in any of our large hospitals as to the number of adults admitted who have not recently had a bath. The medical profession know very well the extent of the need for regular washing among the poorest of the community, who depend upon the cleansing effects of perspiration added to that of clean underclothes. In many cases wounds do not heal because of the dirty condition of the surface of the body, and this, of course, can only be prevented by regular bathing. The importance of a clean skin to the healing of wounds was recognised more effectively by the Japanese in the Russo-Japanese war than, perhaps, by any other nation up to that time. In most of their armies the men, before going into battle, were required to have a hot bath and put on clean clothes. The results showed a great reduction in the contamination of wounds by skin infection.

Facilities for lessening house work.—Many of our old cottages were constructed without any

Housing and Public Health

regard for facilitating the work of the housewife. Washhouses and privies were erected long distances from the dwelling, and many of the things already mentioned, such as rough surfaces, dilapidated walls and floors, and the absence of an internal water supply and sink, all added to the housewife's work. In planning new dwellings this consideration ought to be borne carefully in mind. In town dwellings the presence of a gas cooker is a great labour-saving device. It is at present doubtful whether electric current will ever be produced at a cost which will enable it to be freely used for lighting, heating, and mechanical power in the town dwellings occupied by the artisan classes; but if it could be there would obviously be much saving of domestic labour.

CHAPTER III

The Space Allotted to the Dwelling

SUFFICIENT space must be allowed for the free circulation of air on at least two opposite sides of every house. This space must be so clear of buildings of all kinds and of trees so as to permit also the free access of sunlight. It is the absence of this free air space that constitutes one of the gravest defects of old buildings. Lofty factories or even high walls may block out light and air. A sooty wall absorbs white light so effectively that, in some cases, not more than one-eighth of the light falling on the wall is reflected. In windy weather the question of air space is less important, and were it possible to ensure a considerable amount of wind continuously it would not be so necessary to consider the buildings surrounding a dwelling-house from the point of view of air supply. But we have, of course, to provide for calm weather, when it is necessary to our sense of well-being that there should be an adequate blow-through of air in the dwelling.

In the best town-planned areas the houses

Housing and Public Health

which may be erected to the acre are generally restricted to between eight and fifteen in number, and this in itself is usually sufficient to secure adequate space around dwellings. Again, in good model bye-laws there are stipulations that every dwelling shall on one side front a road of minimal width, and that on the opposite side there shall be a space 200 to 300 sq. ft. in area unoccupied by any building except a water-closet and washhouse. Many other detailed provisions are also made in bye-laws which indirectly secure an adequate supply of external air.

In this connection no question arises as to the composition of the air. It is probable that except for soot and tar and sulphurous acid, and perhaps also certain other gases which are met with in the air, together with road dust of all kinds, the air of all our towns is good and wholesome, if in sufficient abundance. The question of what is best to be done in regard to the open space round houses to be built in the future is dealt with in Chap. V.

Self-contained houses.—There is, perhaps, no single feature which has had more to do with the disastrous effects of bad housing on the health of the people than the fact that a large number of the old houses are not self-contained. By a house being self-contained is meant that it shall be complete in its water supply, drainage, yard, and in every other respect. Houses not self-contained

Environment

are to be deprecated because accommodations which are used in common are looked after badly, and give rise to dirty habits and general carelessness among the tenants, and also to quarrelling. The common courtyard is one of the most frequent sources of trouble. One dirty tenant in a courtyard is a source of annoyance and injury to the rest of the tenants, and all this reacts upon the children. It is impossible for the landlord or for the sanitary authority to hold any one individual responsible for dirty conditions, because one tenant can always blame another, and so such property goes from bad to worse.

It is a common experience that water-closets used in common by a number of families are usually in a dirty and very often repulsive condition. Frequently, such closets have a urinal added, which makes them additionally objectionable, and renders it impossible for women of ordinary modesty to use them. It is indeed remarkable that the people who use these common conveniences have not rebelled years ago against an arrangement so repugnant to elementary decency.

The subject is so important that it is desirable to lay it down as a rule which has but one exception, that all dwellings should be self-contained if they are to be occupied by families, the exception mentioned being the common stairs leading to tenement houses.

Housing and Public Health

From an administrative point of view, every sanitary inspector who has had experience of this class of property will testify how greatly his difficulties are increased by the common use by families of conveniences, yards, water supplies, etc. He will also say how very unsatisfactory the law is at present in regard to the prevention of nuisances arising from "common user." As an example, if water-closets used in common are found to be in a filthy condition and the actual offender cannot be discovered, the law requires that a summons shall be taken out against every person using such closets—men, women, and children! In practice, such action is ridiculous. The common courtyard is, fortunately, becoming deserted by the self-respecting tenants, who appreciate the advantage of a self-contained house. The results have been that houses in most of these common courtyards are now occupied by the least desirable class of tenants, and their condition, therefore, is going from bad to worse.

General drainage and other sanitary fittings.—As already pointed out, it has been the custom in the past to provide only the minimum of sanitary fittings for the slum-dweller. Partly this was done because he was supposed not to need sanitary fittings, but also because he was known to be more or less destructive. But gradually drains have been provided, water-closets put

Environment

in, sinks provided inside the house, and also reasonable facilities for carrying off rain-water. Nothing gives rise to greater friction with tenants than inadequate provision of drainage, water-closets, ashbins, or washing accommodation. As previously stated, it is essential that every house should be self-contained in these respects. In the case of houses using a drain or a water-closet in common, such a drain is frequently situated opposite the front door of one house, and all the tenants have to come to it in order to empty their slop water. Such a proceeding is objected to by the occupier of the particular house, and quarrels result.

The drainage arrangements of the older houses are frequently very defective, mainly because they were laid by builders who did not understand the general principles of drain construction. These drains leaked into cellars or wells, they were not disconnected from the sewers, and were frequently unventilated. In many of the older towns the house drains were built of rubble stones or of bricks, as glazed earthenware pipes were too expensive, and drain gullies were of antiquated types, frequently causing stench.

Midden privies.—There are still towns in England where midden privies of the most objectionable and disease-producing types exist. In other towns pan closets of various types are still in use. In yet other towns there are waste-water

Housing and Public Health

closets of different kinds. All these abominations are inconsistent with the provision of reasonable conditions for cleanliness and the maintenance of good health. It seems almost unnecessary, with the vast experience of past years, to insist that, except in rural areas, there must be no storage of excrement or other foul matter in proximity to the dwelling.

Innumerable reports have been made on the results of such conservancy systems. The experience of Birmingham is similar to that of other towns. During the past fifteen years the removal of pan closets has been rapid and is now complete. In the same period the cases of typhoid fever have fallen from 800 per annum to 20 per annum. The probable explanation of this fall and of many similar reductions is to be found in the fact that excremental matter is no longer stored or allowed to soak into the ground near dwellings, but is removed by a clean-water-carriage system.

Here again, so far as the town cottage dwelling is concerned, there is only one system which is permissible, and that is the clean-water system. Mention has been made of towns in which slop closets have been introduced. In a large number of cases these, either on account of their large fouled surfaces or from their liability to become choked, are unwholesome and disgustingly offensive,

Environment

Removal of solid refuse.—One feature which strikes visitors to a poor-class area, particularly a slum area, is the tendency to collect solid refuse and allow it to lie about. In many towns middens are the only means of collecting and storing this refuse. These middens probably play an equally important part with the privy in spreading disease.

Experience enables us to lay down very definitely the general proposition that for town areas all household refuse should be immediately placed in a covered ashbin, and removed not less frequently than once a week. We now know the part played by accumulations of refuse in causing disease on the one hand by allowing flies to breed and transfer filth from the ashplace to food, and on the other hand by such filth, when dry, being carried as dust into the dwelling. Nothing is more instructive than to watch the way in which flies pass from their breeding places in filth to food inside the houses. If flies are caught, let us say, in a stable manure pit and dusted with flour, it is possible to trace them into the neighbouring houses at regular intervals during the day. Flies cannot, of course, gain access to refuse which is kept covered, but if by chance any should breed in the ashbin the removal of its contents once a week will prevent the eggs from being hatched.

It has been frequently advocated that in the case of cottage dwellings such refuse as has been mentioned should be burned in the kitchen fire. This is a good plan where possible, but in the artisan's dwelling a fire is seldom available during the summer months, as most of the cooking is done by gas stoves. Frequently, too, the amount of vegetable refuse is rather large for the size of the fire.

Surface pollution.—Another feature which generally distinguishes an unwholesome area is the large amount of surface contamination in yards, passages, and streets by organic refuse from the houses and ashpits. It is not widely understood that all such contamination favours the generation of germs, and that these germs are blown about. Cats, dogs, fowl, and pigeons add to the contamination, so that in these unwholesome areas, where people are careless and dirty in their habits, considerable quantities of dried matter from the surface of the yards and roads are blown indiscriminately into the houses, whether these be clean or dirty. It is therefore extremely difficult for the clean tenant to keep his children as free from disease as he would be able to do under more favourable conditions.

The slum-dweller does not understand, again, that water which he has used to wash his hands contains large quantities of organic matter, and also germs from human contamination. Yet it is a common habit among the people living in these

Environment

areas to throw such organically polluted liquids on to the surface of yards and roadways.

Washhouses. — Among the poor the cost of sending washing to a public laundry has, up to the present, been prohibitive. Facilities for washing have been provided, in a few cases, by public washhouses, but in the large majority of cases washing is done at home or in small washhouses common to three or four dwellings, and used on successive days by the various tenants. Washing in these houses is always done under difficulties, and drying also is frequently an inconvenience. The result is dirtiness, less washing being done than would be done under more favourable conditions.

CHAPTER IV

The General Requirements of the Dwelling

MOST of our slum-dwellings are surrounded by
other buildings, and in the centre of our large
towns these buildings are dark and sooty, so that
everything which is to be seen is ugly and repel-
lent. No clean thing and no green thing is within
sight. In many large towns the poorer children,
until they are over school age, seldom, if ever,
visit the country, and except in special instances
public parks, where trees and grass grow healthily,
are not accessible to them. The constant association from early life with soot-stained dwellings,
soot-laden air, and clothing dirtied by soot, tends
to prevent the individual from seeking to better
himself and his condition. The depressing and
demoralising influence of ugliness and dirtiness is
undeniably great.

The presence of soot in the air of a town is not
only unsightly but harmful, a large amount of
sunlight being shut out. Soot in the air causes a
clean and careful housewife to shut up her windows
to keep out the "blacks."

Many medical writers have asserted that the
presence of soot and sulphurous acid in the air is

General Requirements

a potent cause of lung trouble among town dwellers, and have brought forward figures which apparently show this to be the case. As already pointed out, the shutting out of the actinic or ultra-violet rays of sunlight by a cloud of smoke is a matter of great importance to health. The difference is very noticeable to a photographer, who in the country can frequently take in an instant a photograph which would require an exposure a thousand times as long in a town.

Transit facilities.— It may be considered somewhat anomalous to mention the subject of transit facilities as a requisite for housing, but when it is borne in mind that towns now spread over vast areas of ground, and that every indication points to their being spread over even larger areas in the future, the provision of transit facilities is seen to be of great importance in this connection.

While it is not desirable that everybody should work in the centre and live in a suburb, large numbers will always require to travel backwards and forwards between their homes in the suburbs and their offices or warehouses in the business centre. For this reason it is important that the authorities dealing with town planning and the building of houses should be in very close touch with those controlling the means of transit.

Means of recreation.— It is necessary, in enumerating the needs of dwellers in small house

Housing and Public Health

property, to consider also the provision of reasonable means of recreation. For little children there is a great need for small playgrounds, where they can be in the open air and more or less under control. Again, for boys and girls of older growth, playing fields are needed, and for adults, parks, theatres, gymnasia, libraries, etc. Most of these requirements are absent from the slum area.

Dryness of site.—In the vast majority of cases a town has increased in area despite the nature of its soil, and so long as no attempt is made to build on areas which are flooded, and therefore water-logged, there is not much evidence that the nature of the soil or its water content plays any important part in the production of illness, if reasonable precautions are taken to cover the site with an impervious layer of concrete or asphalt. In many towns, however, there are areas where the soil is positively wet and where flooding occasionally takes place. These areas ought to be reserved for parks, or for works purposes.

A great deal of attention has been paid to the composition of the soil on which towns are built. There is very little evidence, however, that a clay soil differs hygienically from sandy soil having the same elevation and slope. Many towns entirely built on a clay foundation have no larger proportion of cases of rheumatism than towns built on a sandy subsoil.

General Requirements

Aspect.—The importance of aspect has already been insisted upon. Generally speaking, it is possible to arrange for most of the new streets of a town to run from east to west, so that the houses face south, south-west, or south-east, in which case the living-rooms can be placed on the south side of the house and get the benefit of the sun. If one of these aspects can be obtained, from a purely health point of view south-east is probably better than south-west for living-rooms.

Cellars.—Cellars are, on the whole, undesirable in cottage property. This is mainly due to the fact that a cellar, if ventilated, causes cold, damp air to be drawn into the dwelling when it is warm, by convection currents. Again, with the poorer class of occupiers the cellar frequently becomes a place of deposit for rubbish. It is not a convenient place in which to store coal, because this has to be carried up a flight of steps when required for use. It is wise, therefore, to avoid cellars.

Trade nuisances.— In the older parts of our large towns, interspersed between the houses are many workshops and factories, and some of them give rise to intolerable nuisances, which it is difficult to prevent under the ordinary laws of the country. Smoke and grit from steam-engine chimneys or from metallurgical furnaces, dust from the exhaust fans of factories, evil smells from

Housing and Public Health

gut scraping, tripe boiling, and a hundred other industries, all make the conditions of life unwholesome in the central areas of towns, and should be entirely prevented in the newer areas. In town planning, therefore, it is most important to obtain powers to prevent such trades from being established in residential districts.

CHAPTER V

The Future Housing of the People

Two lines of work are indicated in this title, viz. (1) The building of new houses, and (2) the reconstruction of old areas in such a way as to make them sufficient for the minimal requirements of healthy living.

Before dealing with the first of these subjects it is well to consider a few general principles.

First, it is very desirable that the best standard should be adopted now, so that we may not have to amend our buildings in the future. It would, for instance, be a fatal mistake to build labourers' dwellings without a parlour and a bathroom, or without a number of other amenities, although there may be a doubt in the minds of many people as to the reasonable necessity for them. The present book is written from the viewpoint that no attempt should be made to come down to the standard of the cottage at a rental of 2s. 6d. per week for the agricultural labourer, or of 4s. 6d. a week for the town worker.

Another general principle is that care must be

Housing and Public Health

taken to avoid conditions which, as yet, have not been sufficiently tested. For instance, it may be argued that tenement dwellings will meet all the reasonable requirements of the community, and statistics may be brought forward, as in the case of the Peabody Buildings, to show that such dwellings have very low mortality-rates. What, however, holds good of selected tenants for such buildings will not be applicable generally.

There is a good deal of evidence to indicate that tenement dwellings are injurious to the health of children, but unless the most careful inquiry is made this is not very evident. It has been shown, however, in recent years, that in many of the towns where tenement dwellings are most abundant the number of children suffering from rickets is greatly in excess of the number in towns where cottages predominate. Professor Noel Paton, of Glasgow, has demonstrated a fact which was known before to dog owners, viz. that puppies if kept in a well-ventilated room will develop rickets, while others from the same litter and fed in the same way, if allowed to run about in the open, remain free from that disease.

Tenement dwellings have been erected mainly because land was expensive, but in reality it was the tenements that made the land expensive, and where they do not already exist it would be a disastrous mistake to introduce them, except in

Housing Schemes

small numbers, for adults. And if tenements are provided it will always be difficult to prevent them from being occupied by families in which there are young children.

Building schemes of the future.—By far the most important advance made by Parliament in recent years in the interests of the housing of the people was the passing of Town Planning legislation in 1909. There was no doubt in the minds of those who originated this system that the main, and one might almost say the only, object of town planning was to enable dwellings, and particularly small dwellings, to be arranged in such a way as to give them a really healthy environment. It is not sufficiently recognised, however, that town planning is a necessary adjunct of housing, for in many towns the one question has been referred to one authority and the other to another authority. In the most important recent book on the law relating to Housing all reference to town planning has been omitted, because town planning "properly forms no part of the Housing of the Working Classes Acts, either in fact or according to the definitions in the Act of 1909."

The essential section in the Housing, Town Planning, etc., Act of 1909, viz. Section 54 (1), is simple and short; it is as follows:

A town planning scheme may be made in accordance with the provisions of this part of this Act as respects

Housing and Public Health

any land which is in course of development or appears to be likely to be used for building purposes, *with the general object of securing proper sanitary conditions, amenity, and convenience* in connection with the laying out and use of the land and of any neighbouring lands.

The first essential, therefore, in regard to the housing of the people is to secure a town planning scheme, so that "proper sanitary conditions, amenity, and convenience" may be obtained.

At the present time such a scheme can only be made for land which is in course of development or likely to be built upon, and although this will include most of the land in proximity to towns, it is important that the provision should, in the near future, be further extended, so as to deal on somewhat similar lines with areas already built on.

From the point of view of housing, it is desirable, in making a town plan, to separate the manufacturing areas from the residential areas at the outset, because each of these types of area requires special treatment of its own.

In the case of the manufacturing area the roads, the facilities for railway and canal traffic, the facilities for cheap motive power, such as that from Mond gas, or electric power, have to be taken into consideration. It is almost as important to provide facilities for the manufacturer as it is to promote the building of residences for the worker. Neither can do without the other. It is desirable, too, in the case of manufacturing areas to have the

68

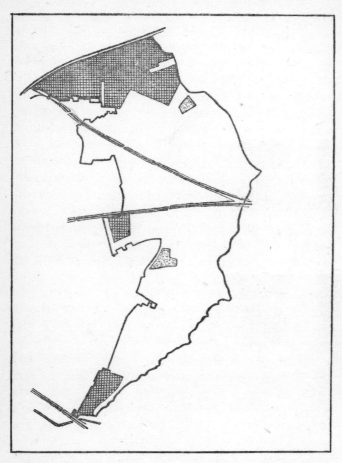

Fig. 2.—To show factory areas (cross-hatched) in a town-planned area.

Housing and Public Health

residences of the workpeople not too far from the factories, so that they may be able to go home and have their meals with their families, and thus save expense and secure for themselves and all the members of their families good and sufficient food.

By removing factories and business premises to a reasonable distance from the residential area one is able to secure to the residential area freedom from smoke, dust, noise, and traffic. Having planned out the areas most suitable for business purposes, it is then possible not only to lay out the rest of the area for dwellings of various grades, but to allocate sites for allotments, playing-fields, shops, theatres, churches, and all the numerous other amenities which go to make up a healthy residential area. (Fig. 2.)

In arranging town planning schemes the best possible provision should be made for transit, so that the people in any particular area can as quickly as possible get to other areas, either for business or for social purposes. All of these questions come under the heading of Convenience in the Town Planning Act. By making roads wide it is possible to arrange various types of fast tramways or other means of travel, so that time may be saved in getting from one area to another, and if such roads are planned well in advance of their coming into use they can be made attractive features, instead of hideously ugly, as many of them are to-day.

Housing Schemes

Again, while for main roads, and perhaps for subsidiary roads, the essential condition is width, for fast traffic, it is desirable that the residential road should be narrow and as free as possible from traffic. This may be secured by contriving

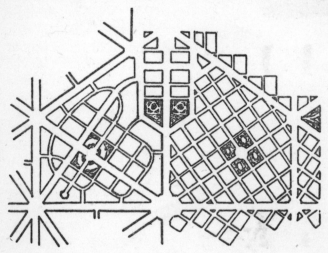

Fig. 3.

Well-contrived roads : few available for through traffic.   Ill-contrived roads : all available for through traffic.

(*From the Report of the Tudor Walters Committee.*)

that the road leads nowhere, as shown in the accompanying diagram (Fig. 3). Such roads are cheaper to make, because they are narrow, there is economy in the cleaning and watering, there is much less dust, and, by reason of their taking no

Housing and Public Health

more traffic than is needed for the houses in the road, there is less noise and vibration. Quietness, and absence of the vibration which is so constant a feature of heavy modern road traffic, are important considerations.

The area allocated for residential purposes will, of course, contain the parks, playing fields, allotments, institutes, swimming bath, etc.

To secure amenity is one of the reasons given in the Act for making a town plan. As already indicated, if substantial progress is to be made in bettering the lives of the working classes, probably one method will be that of providing greater amenity in the surroundings of their homes, as well as in the interior accommodation. When we come to consider the rebuilding of the slums it will be found that the question of providing amenity in the rebuilt areas has not yet received the attention that it deserves. As a result, many of the schemes for building the central areas will probably fail, sufficient attention not having been given to securing for the workers' dwellings reasonably good surroundings. It is important that the women and children, at any rate, should be able to escape at frequent intervals from the awful monotony of soot-begrimed bricks and mortar, and it should be possible for them, therefore, to get without difficulty into playing spaces or parks which are green and pretty. Much of the stunted

Housing Schemes

and degenerate mental outlook of the slum-dweller is due to the absence of pleasant surroundings to his dwelling.

The provision of proper sanitary conditions is stated in the Act as the first object of the town plan, but it is here presented as of less importance than the obtaining of amenity and convenience. Already there exists in our Public Health Acts and our building regulations sufficient power to secure sanitary conditions up to a certain point. The additional sanitary conditions of importance which the Act enables us to obtain are the limitation of the number of dwellings, the avoidance of long rows of houses, the prevention of noxious trades in close proximity to dwellings, and the avoidance of other nuisances.

Number of dwelling-houses per acre. — In Schedule 5, paragraph 5, of the Housing, Town Planning, etc., Act, 1909, there is a requirement that a town plan, before it can be approved by the Local Government Board, shall not only state the number of buildings (not dwellings) per acre, but also "the height and character" of these buildings, so that there may be a reasonable safeguard against crowding of the area with undesirable buildings.

The Local Government Board, in a circular dated March 18th, 1918, addressed to local authorities, recommend that for houses for the working

Housing and Public Health

classes not more than 12 per acre should be erected in urban districts, and that in rural districts the number should not be more than 8 per acre. In the first town planning scheme approved by Parliament, viz. that of Quinton, Harborne, and Edgbaston, in Birmingham, a limit of 12 houses per acre is placed on each land unit, the unit being for practical purposes the land belonging to one owner. There is, however, a reservation that in any land unit the maximum number on any one acre may be as high as 20. The object of this reservation is to enable houses to be built on small areas of ground, while the rest of the land is allotted to open spaces. As an illustration, 60 houses might be built on three acres of ground, provided two acres were set apart for the use of the tenants as an open space.

In the second town planning scheme, viz. that for East Birmingham, several standards were adopted for different areas, 12, 15, and 18 dwelling-houses respectively being allowed per acre. In practice it is found that wherever a larger number of houses than 12 are provided per acre there is a sense of congestion to a greater or less extent, depending on the slope and general lie of the land, while there are very numerous examples of areas where 6, 8, and 10 houses per acre are provided, which give really adequate space and privacy. It must always be remembered that pro-

Housing Schemes

vision has to be made for the careless as well as for the careful tenant, and that, similarly, people have to be provided for to whom gardening in any form is distasteful, and it is desirable, therefore, in planning new areas, to make provision for these various needs and tastes. The Birmingham scheme of requiring for such tenants an open space is a good and wholesome one. Bournville has, on an average, 8 houses per acre, Port Sunlight 10, Hampstead Garden Suburb 8, and Letchworth (smallest) 12. From these figures, and from an inspection of the areas, I am strongly of opinion that there should not be a larger number of dwelling-houses on any one acre than 12, except in the case of tenants who do not want gardens.

The lay-out.—By this is meant the general scheme of arrangement of dwellings, roads, parks, institutes, and buildings of all kinds. Usually this is a matter for a surveyor, with the help of a good contoured map and a knowledge of what is wanted. As a general rule, it is important to secure that, as far as practicable, streets should run in such directions that the dwellings get the maximum amount of sunlight on one side, and that the streets should give the maximum of convenience to the inhabitants.

Mixing the classes.—One feature which has not yet been generally recognised as desirable in the laying-out of a scheme is the need for

Housing and Public Health

housing all classes of the community together, instead of establishing an "east end " and a "west end " in our new areas. Perhaps the most excellent town plan which has ever been made in this country was that for the new town of Edinburgh. Here, in 1767, provision was made in advance for the housing of all classes of the community together, and thus preventing separation of the classes. Edinburgh has profited by this, perhaps, more than by almost any other feature of the scheme. The old town plan was departed from many years ago, but the feature of housing different classes together or near each other has remained. Nobody is inconvenienced, the poorer classes are largely benefited, while the better classes are benefited to an even greater extent by being brought into close contact with their poorer neighbours and realising their difficulties.

There is no reason why, in a new town plan, areas quite close together should not be set aside for groups of houses of different classes, so that there may be no separation of classes.

Details of the plan.—The preparation of the details of a town-planning scheme need not be completed until the land is actually required for building, provided that the main features of the scheme are decided on long beforehand.

It may be pointed out that one great advantage of good planning of an estate for artisans' dwell-

Housing Schemes

ings is that it cheapens the dwellings by allowing all of the land to be made use of.

Straight versus curved roads. — As already pointed out, the carriage-way in the majority of the roads in residential areas need not be wide so long as the buildings on either side of the road are sufficiently set back. Given such a road, whether wide or narrow, it is desirable to avoid straightness. A slight curve makes a surprising difference in the appearance of any road, and particularly of a road which is tree-planted. A deviation equal to the interval between the houses on the opposite sides of the road in every quarter of a mile of length amply fulfils this condition, and gives a pleasant tree-planted prospect at every turn.

The set-back. — All dwellings in residential areas should be set back from the footpath. Whether the road be a wide traffic road or a narrow one, this should always be provided for. Such a set-back is necessary on health grounds: there are less noise, less vibration, less dust, and greater privacy.

CHAPTER VI

General Block Plan of the House

THE general block plan of an artisan's house may be either narrow and deep, or wide and shallow. The narrow and deep house is the common type suggested by the builder who desires to provide something cheap. It has many disadvantages as well as some advantages. It gives less light and air, but is warmer than houses with a wide frontage.

Frequently it is desirable to adapt the shape of the house to the lie of the ground. Hilly sites are met with where long and narrow buildings require less excavation than deep buildings, provided the roads run along contour lines. On such hilly sites it is important, and indeed on any site it is desirable, to make quite certain that every building shåll be so arranged as not to keep off direct sunlight from other buildings.

The accompanying sketch (Fig. 4) indicates how very much more obstructive to direct sunlight a building is in winter than in summer, and it must be borne in mind that the winter sunshine lasts a

General Block Plan

much shorter number of hours than the summer sunshine, and is less actinic. It is important, therefore, to take steps to conserve the sun's rays during the winter to a larger extent than during the summer.

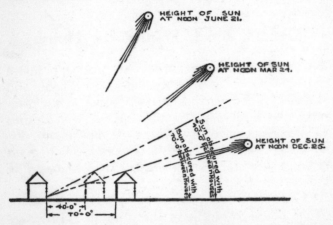

Fig. 4.—To illustrate the greater obstructiveness of buildings to direct sunlight in winter.

(*From the Report of the Tudor Walters Committee.*)

To fit houses to roads with varying gradients is by no means an easy matter for any surveyor, and therefore the arrangement of the houses is of great importance.

Size of the building.—With 10 houses to the acre, each house would have 484 square yards, while in a congested area, with 40 cottages, the average would be 121 square yards. When

Housing and Public Health

the roadways and set-backs and area of the houses are taken into consideration, the garden space for such houses is small, and even with 10 houses to the gross acre it does not allow of the production of all the green vegetables required in an ordinary dwelling. Mr. Raymond Unwin and others have demonstrated by plans and by statistical methods that the limitation of houses to 10 per gross acre is economical, for this will give a valuable garden at a cheaper rate per square yard than in the case of houses crowded to 25 per acre. He has shown that, while the tenant, for all the additional advantage of extra garden, pays something less than one shilling per week in rent, he gets as a set-off a garden of such a size and productiveness as to be much more than a *quid pro quo*. It has also been stated on high authority that the limitation of houses per acre does not necessarily mean that the owner of the estate has the value of his land greatly reduced. A good deal of attention has been paid to this subject by Mr. Aldridge in his work on "Town Planning."

Back roads.—In a large number of our English working-class town districts the custom of providing a back road for the removal of refuse still exists. The *raison d'être* of these back roads, viz. the removal of ashpit refuse, no longer exists, because no town can afford to allow ashpits, and therefore, in our future town planning, there is no need to

General Block Plan

provide for these expensive and insanitary roads. The removal of refuse and the taking in of coal and manure for the garden can be provided for either by passage-ways between each of two houses, or by paths round the backs of the houses if they are built in fours, as shown in the accompanying diagrams (Figs. 5, 6).

Storage of refuse. — Long experience and scientific investigation have now clearly defined the best method of storing household refuse and

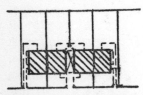 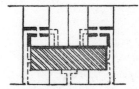

Fig. 5.—Four cottages with covered passage in the centre, and side passages for the two outer ones.

Fig. 6.—Four cottages without covered passage.

(From the Report of the Tudor Walters Committee.)

making provision for its removal. A bin, if of good quality, will last fifteen or twenty years in the suburbs of most of our towns, and if such a bin is kept covered no permanent shed is needed, and so expense is saved.

Privacy of back premises.—This is as essential as the privacy of front rooms. It is therefore undesirable that the tenants of one house should be allowed to pass across the garden or yard of

Housing and Public Health

the next house to gain access to their own back premises. The working man, as well as the better-class tenant, desires that his house should have privacy, and this must be kept in view in planning.

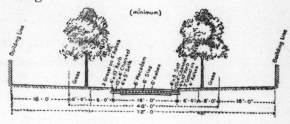

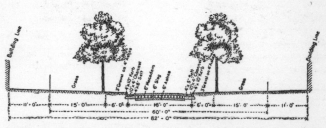

Fig. 7.—Types of narrow and cheap roads for residential districts where traffic is light.
(From the Harborne Town Planning Order.)

Roadways.—The accompanying plans (Fig. 7) indicate different types of narrow roadways, with the houses set back. In the case of the first plan the carriage-way is 18 ft. wide, each footpath is 3 ft. wide, there is a grass margin of 5 ft. between the footpath and the fence, and the distance between the houses is 72 ft. These are probably minimal standards, and may be increased in other areas.

Roadways should be as dustless and noiseless as possible. The Report to the Local Government Board in regard to them contains suggestions which may be quoted.

" We suggest . . . the following as possible economies in the construction of streets :—

" (a) Carriage-ways to be reduced in width where their length and the planning of the area sufficiently secure the absence of through traffic, or, in the event of suitable powers being conferred, in cases where traffic can be limited.

" (b) Such carriage-ways to be constructed with a sufficient bed of ashes, clinker, or other suitable materials when the subsoil is of a clayey nature, with a foundation of rubble or hardcore, of which a thickness of 9 in. should suffice, and finished with either—

(i.) 3 in. of tar macadam, or
(ii.) 4 in. of macadam, or
(iii.) 6 in. of gravel flints or other approved material.

" (c) Where a suitable refuse-destructor clinker is available, the use of this for foundations should be considered either in its natural condition or, where expedient, in the form of a layer of concrete.

" (d) Curbing and channelling to be reduced to the minimum or to be omitted altogether, as required by the circumstances of the street.

" (e) The footpaths on quite short roads on one or both sides to be omitted or to be greatly reduced in width.

Housing and Public Health

"(f) Any necessary footpaths to be constructed of 4 in. of rubble, clinker, or hardcore foundation paved with a strip of natural or artificial stone paving, of hard brick paving where suitable local paving is available, or of $2\frac{1}{2}$ in. of tar macadam, to a width of from 3 to 4 ft., and to be finished for the remainder of the width with a layer of 2 or 3 in. of clean binding gravel or other approved material, a light kerb or a grass verge being provided."

Drainage questions.— A great deal of over-elaboration of detail in drainage has been required in recent years as a result of our modern bye-laws. Generally speaking, the shorter the drains are in length and the smaller the size of the pipes, provided they are large enough for the work, the better the scheme. Unfortunately, those who design drainage systems frequently have but little experience of the working of their schemes. Hence the over-elaboration, with added expenditure and without good results.

Two systems have come into operation in recent years. One is known as the separate system, because in this there is a system of drainage for rain water and surface water from the yards and roads, while another system takes off the discharge from water-closets, sinks, baths, etc. It was thought that by providing such a separate system the rain water, etc., could be run into the nearest stream, while the sewage was taken for treatment to the disposal works, and that in this way great economy would be effected, both in the lessened amount of sewage to be treated and the lessened size of the sewers to take the drainage.

In practice, however, this dual system is extremely objectionable. It doubles the number of drainage pipes about every dwelling-house, it doubles the number of sewers in every street, it doubles the volume of evil smells which come from sewers in the streets, it does not allow of clean water only being run into rivers, because the washing from paved streets is found to be very much polluted, and it causes material difficulties at sewage works, because the sewage is always concentrated. While rivers are in flood there is not, as a rule, much harm in allowing the overflow from sewers to pass into them.

The combined system has the advantage of shortness mentioned in the first paragraph of this section, besides giving to the drains and sewers a better scouring during rainstorms, and thus keeping them cleaner and in better condition and freer from smell.

The intercepting trap.—It is desirable that every house should have an interception trap. A good many doubts have been expressed as to the value of such traps, and the subject is discussed in a recent Report to the Local Government Board. Most modern bye-laws, however, require interception traps. This is not the place to argue whether they are necessary or not. Sufficient to

Housing and Public Health

say that if an interception trap is provided in cottage property, one of the closed traps of the Buchan type is better than one which is at the outlet to a manhole. In practice it will be found that in cottage property the latter gets blocked up five times more frequently than the former.

The interception trap requires to have attached to it a fresh-air inlet, properly guarded by means of a mica flap ventilator.

Drains.—Where drains are provided which pass in close proximity to the dwelling-house they should be surrounded with concrete. This is expensive, but in time it will repay the cost. Wherever the fall is away from the dwelling there is no necessity to provide concrete. Cottage drains need not be laid more than from 15 to 18 in. below the surface, except where the lie of the land requires greater depth, or where a cartway passes over them.

Drain law.—Undoubtedly the thing which has made the drainage of cottage property expensive is the rather ridiculous state of the law with regard to the definition of a drain. At the present time it is not infrequent to find six or more separate drains from as many houses passing down one narrow passage. This is done to avoid the combined or common drain, which would have been much the better from a sanitary point of view, but which, since it would have taken the drainage from more than one house, would have become a sewer. From a health point of view it is in every way better to provide but one drain for a number of cottages, say up to twelve or fourteen, than to provide a separate drain for each house. In the former case there is a better flush and a more uniform volume of drainage, and the expense is, of course, much less. One interception trap does instead of twelve or fourteen, and it is possible, therefore, to have one good drain instead of a number of inferior ones.

It is greatly to be desired that the law relating to drains should be simplified. As showing how unsatisfactory is the present state of things, it has been contended that rain-water gutters are common sewers repairable by the local authority if they take the rain water from more than one house belonging to the same owner.

Waste pipes.—Until recent years sink and bath wastes in cottage property were not trapped, but, in accordance with the requirements of the model bye-laws of the Local Government Board, were discharged into a channel some distance away from a gully. Only those who have lived in houses with such waste pipes will recognise how extremely offensive they become owing to a coating of decomposing fat and other filth being deposited on the interior surface, and as they have

Housing and Public Health

no trap they act as inlet ventilators to the scullery or bathroom of the house, with the result that in these rooms most offensive odours are frequently noticed. It is practically certain that occasionally these evil smells are a predisposing cause of sore throat and other affections. Modern practice indicates that every waste pipe should be trapped, and that it is better to discharge waste pipes into a gully than over a gully.

Yard surfaces.—In all cottage property there is need for a small paved yard, because it is necessary to empty offensive or organically contaminated liquids into a gully outside rather than into a sink or water-closet. It is important, therefore, that the area around the gully and around waste pipes should be paved, and should have a fall towards the gully, so that no soiling of the ground may take place.

Gully traps.—There is little to be said in regard to gully traps, except that most of those now on the market are excellent in pattern. The simpler their construction the better, for nobody likes cleaning and adjusting the internal arrangements of a gully. There is, however, one point of considerable importance in regard to gullies for cottage properties, i.e. the grid or grating should be hinged. Where children are allowed to play about, the grid, if it is loose, is frequently removed, and so things get into the gullies which are washed into the drain, with the result that blocking takes place.

Fences and walls.—The former custom of building high brick walls round every cottage garden or every cottage back yard added to the expense and to the ugliness of the outlook. In most cases a light post and rail or post and wire-netting fence, or a hedge, is better than a brick wall. A good hedge is effective and much more satisfactory than any wall. Circumstances, however, will dictate what is best in the interests of efficiency and security. What is to be avoided is an accumulation of brick and stone walls in the area behind dwelling-houses.

CHAPTER VII

The Accommodations of a Cottage

It has already been pointed out that in designing a cottage care must be taken to provide for the future rather than for the past. The type of cottage here dealt with is one for an ordinary artisan's family, but obviously there must be exceptional families, and therefore exceptional houses will be required. In every town there are instances in which one room and a scullery might suffice for a widow living alone, or where the three bedrooms suggested in the following pages would be quite inadequate to the size of the family, but these exceptions require no further notice.

Without doubt the most useful family house is one having three bedrooms and two day rooms. Such a size is suitable to a larger number of families than any other. If the family is small and remains so, a room can be let to a lodger. It is seldom that the three-bedroomed house is too small for the artisan's family.

The parlour.—Custom has a powerful influence in determining a preference for one day room

Accommodations of a Cottage

or for two, but it is likely that custom in this respect will change; indeed, there is no doubt that it is already changing, the large majority of respectable artisans liking to have a parlour. It is a real advantage in the family life, it is a source of pride and a convenience in entertaining friends, it is useful for interviews, particularly is it useful for those of the family who have lessons to learn, it can be used for those who are sick, it enables many articles of value to be kept out of harm's way, and there is little doubt that before long it will be demanded as essential for every self-respecting family. The provision of a parlour also enables better accommodation to be arranged on the first floor.

The scullery. — Having decided that a parlour is necessary, we have next to consider whether it is wise ever to attempt to combine the scullery and living-room. In many parts of the country it is customary for the living-room to have a sink, frequently a washing boiler, and often a gas cooker and food cupboard. But from living in such rooms, and visiting them and inquiring of the artisans themselves, I have no doubt as to the desirability of providing, as a minimal requirement in every family house, a separate scullery, conveniently placed in relation to the living-room. Under all conditions washing in the kitchen is objectionable.

Housing and Public Health

To a large extent the preparation of food, and perhaps to a lesser extent the cooking of it, in the living-room are inconvenient and unpleasant. All those who have experienced the convenience of having a good gas cooker in a separate scullery say that they would not return to the discomfort and muddle entailed by cooking in the ordinary living-room.

It is really important, in the interests of the occupants, that there should be good facilities for cooking and washing. It is equally important that reasonable facilities should be provided for the taking of meals in a room separate from that in which cooking, washing and other operations are going on.

In practice a scullery of approximately 60 sq. ft. of floor space gives sufficient accommodation for a deep sink, a washing copper, a gas cooker, and the necessary shelving for storage. A width of 6 ft. is sufficient to enable it to be used as a passage to the back garden, so as to avoid the necessity for a separate passage, or the use of the living-room as a passage. In such a scullery clothes can be dried in wet weather, and, in the country cottage, bread can be baked.

Size of the living-room and parlour.—The living-room is the most important room in the house, and the only one in which the whole family regularly assemble. It should, therefore, be well

Accommodations of a Cottage

arranged as regards dimensions. 'An oblong room is much more convenient and commodious than a square one, and is structurally more economical,

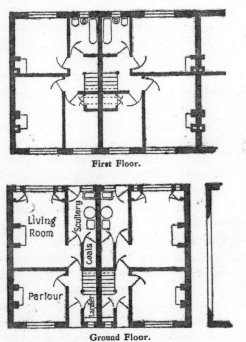

First Floor.

Ground Floor.

Fig. 8.—Plan of good type of narrow-fronted cottages, facing north.
(*Designed by Mr. E. W. Turner.*)

because the joists required are shorter. The living-room should always face south, south-east,

93

or south-west, and be regarded as the important room in the dwelling-house. It may be made to face the street, or to face the back garden, whichever happens to be the proper aspect. (Figs. 8, 9.) The position of doors, windows and fireplace should be carefully studied, so as to prevent as far as practicable draughty corners.

Fig. 8 shows a living-room with one door only; in this case there is a French window. The floor space of such a living-room may vary from approximately 120 sq. ft. upwards. A good working figure is about 180 sq. ft., say 15 ft. by 12 ft.

The parlour should usually be smaller than the living-room. Here, again, a long narrow room is much more convenient than a square one. A floor area of 120 sq. ft. is suggested as a suitable minimum of size.

Hall and stairs.—It is important that the smallest possible area should be occupied by the hall, passages, staircase, and landings. Long narrow passages are very inconvenient and often gloomy. Stairs for family use should not be less than 3 ft. wide, and should as far as possible be free from winders, i.e. steps which are wider at one end than at the other. Few are aware of the amount of maiming caused by steep stairs with winders, but it is difficult to avoid these without increasing the size of the house.

The washhouse.—It has been assumed that

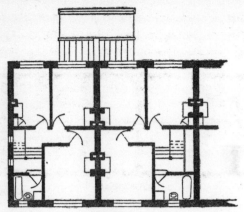

First Floor.

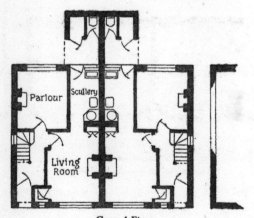

Ground Floor.

Fig. 9.—Plan of similar cottages to those shown in Fig. 8, facing south.

(*Designed by Mr. E. W. Turner.*)

95

Housing and Public Health

the house of the future will still continue to do the whole or the main part of the family washing at home. Public washhouses or other communal

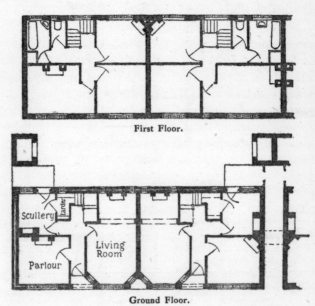

First Floor.

Ground Floor.

Fig. 10.—Plan of pair of cottages with wide fronts, facing south.
(*Designed by Mr. E. W. Turner.*)

systems will never prevent the necessity for some washing being done almost daily in houses where there are young families. Such minor washing is also needed for adults. Provision must therefore be made in the house for the boiling of clothes.

Accommodations of a Cottage

There appears to be no need for a separate wash-house if a washing boiler and a deep sink are provided in the ordinary scullery. An additional building is thus saved outside.

Water-closet accommodation. — The water-closet accommodation provided for an artisan's family in the past has ordinarily been in a separate building in the garden or yard. The idea involved in such separate outside building is a relic of the past, when all cottages were provided with midden privies. Such accommodation was then impossible inside the dwelling, but with our more modern fittings there is nothing insanitary in having the water-closet inside, so long as it can be sufficiently isolated not to be a nuisance to the adjoining rooms. In many cottages the water-closet is situated inside the building, but approached from the outside. This is a better arrangement than having any variety of outside water-closet, because there is scarcely any part of this country in which outside water-closets are not liable to have the water pipes connected with them frozen up at intervals in winter, even where special precautions are taken to protect the pipes.

In middle-class dwellings, where only one water-closet is provided it is usually placed upstairs, frequently in the bathroom. There is no objection on sanitary grounds to its being placed in the bathroom; indeed, this position is be-

H   97

coming more frequent. The upstairs water-closet is of great use to the artisan's family as a labour-saving device, for it acts as a slop sink, and does away with the necessity for carrying dirty water downstairs. Some of the best types of cottages have a water-closet in the bathroom upstairs and an additional water-closet in an outhouse.

The real objection to the upstairs water-closet is that children and others are liable to carry mud upstairs on their boots, but the comfort in sickness and in its greater privacy, together with its labour-saving value, make the upstairs water-closet preferable to one that is downstairs. The extra cost for an upstairs water-closet in a bathroom need not be considered in comparison with the comfort involved, the security which is provided for cleanliness, and the freedom from damage by frost.

The larder.—Only very simple provision need be made for the storage of perishable food. The food store or larder must be on the north or northeast side of the house. It should be away from the chimney flues, and outside the range of evil smells from drain openings or water-closets. The window should be covered with a layer of gauze to keep out flies; no light other than the window is required. A floor area of about 20 ft. is as large as is ever required. This will satisfy the needs of any economical housewife.

Accommodations of a Cottage

The coal store.—The chief requirements of a coal store are that it should be on a level with the rooms in which the coal is used. It is therefore undesirable to have coal stored in a cellar, or far away from the house. A coal store 6 ft. by 5 ft. will permit of a full load of coal being stored, with some room for wood and other things.

The bathroom.—I have already expressed a decided opinion that from a health point of view every dwelling should have a bathroom (p. 47). It may be contended that the plumbing for a bath, lavatory and water-closet upstairs adds so much to the cost of a labourer's cottage as to be unjustifiable, but these things ought to be regarded as among the reasonable requirements of everyday family life. The additional cost on the rent of such an installation means from 1s. 6d. to 2s. per week, but from a medical point of view this is a justifiable expenditure.

Bedrooms.—Obviously these should vary in size. It is well to remember that the broad English bed, capable of holding two or more people, is likely to give place in the near future to the single bed used so much in other parts of the world. This has the great advantage of less personal contact, and, therefore, of spreading less infection.

Each bedroom should have a fireplace and a

Housing and Public Health

window, and if a fireplace cannot be obtained, then a special ventilator at the opposite side of the room to the window should be provided, so that there may be a through draught. The chief feature in the design of a bedroom is the securing that it shall be of such a shape as to enable beds and other furniture to be conveniently placed. It is also important that the window should be so arranged that in almost any weather part of it may remain open.

Bedrooms on the ground floor.—There is no known reason other than sentiment against the use of rooms on the ground floor as bedrooms, and therefore, in the minimal standard cottage which is here described, there is no reason why the parlour downstairs may not either permanently or temporarily be made into a bedroom if need be. Very large experience has been obtained of the use of bedrooms on the ground floor in many countries of the world, among them Scotland and Ireland. While there is no evidence that this arrangement is injurious to health, in England prejudice against it is strong, and in many cases overcrowding of bedrooms occurs simply because the inmates will not use an empty ground-floor room.

Attic rooms.—In a well-planned house no space should be allowed to remain useless. In many instances it is possible to arrange for reason-

Accommodations of a Cottage

ably good bedrooms in the attic. Such bedrooms require to be ceiled and made habitable in every way. But apart from the use of such habitable rooms, space is often wasted in the roof which could conveniently be made use of for general storage purposes. Such space is useful, even if it can only be approached by means of a movable ladder through a hatchway, because in the course of years there are few thrifty families which do not accumulate materials of all kinds that require to be stored away.

Cupboards and shelves.—Much attention has been paid to the need for utilising every available space in an artisan's dwelling for cupboards or for shelving, and many modern plans of such dwellings provide these essential features in abundance; but it cannot be too frequently pointed out that the provision of these adjuncts costs a good deal of money. It is well to remember also that the artisan requires some accommodation for his bicycle or the perambulator. Usually this is provided underneath the stairs. Here also a hat-and-coat rail can be fixed.

Cost of the house. — The question of cost need not be entered into in very great detail in these pages, but obviously it is impossible to deal with the problem of housing for the artisan classes without continuously bearing it in mind. In addition to the provision of sufficient accommo-

Housing and Public Health

dation and of the amenities essential to healthy living, it is necessary, if the house is to justify itself, that it should be erected and let at the least possible cost, and therefore every item in the planning, the lay-out, the building, and the materials will have to be carefully considered from the point of view of economy. In the case of the town cottage, it is desirable that it should be put on the market as an investment into which the artisan himself may put his savings, so that he may have a real stake in the country and a real interest in seeing that his surroundings are well managed. Unless he can get value for his money it will be impossible ever to suggest to him that he should become the owner of the house in which he dwells.

Economy should be secured in such ways as these :

(*a*) Unnecessary passages, landings, and expensive projections from the rectangular building should be avoided.

(*b*) The building materials should be so selected as to secure quality at the least cost.

(*c*) The site should be so laid out as to avoid excessive cost in the first instance.

(*d*) Unnecessary expense is frequently incurred by the employment of middle men, who act as financiers and inflate the cost of the land and of the building.

Accommodations of a Cottage

(*e*) Such matters as the grouping of chimney flues often enable considerable saving to be effected without curtailing the convenience of the house.

(*f*) Unnecessary and often ugly decoration of the exterior should be avoided. A good design is frequently spoilt by over-ornamentation. Variety can be obtained by well considered differences in design and materials.

(*g*) The building materials of the district should be used.

(*h*) Money is often wasted upon the construction of roofs.

(*i*) Standardisation is possible without producing monotony or loss of efficiency.

The various items in the cost of fourteen suburban cottages, given in percentages, are here copied from the Report to the Local Government Board of the Committee on Building Construction (Cd. 9191).

The table shows what a large percentage of the total cost is for labour. If one takes the labour involved in manufacturing the various articles required and in building, one is impressed with the necessity for using all devices for labour-saving in the building trade in order to cheapen the artisan's dwelling.

Housing and Public Health

	Cost per cent.
Timber, manufactured and unmanufactured	17·48
Bricks	9·80
Roof tiles, ridge, etc.	1·65
Glazed and floor tiles	0·48
Sanitary ware and pipes	2·30
Portland cement	2·12
Plaster and mortars	3·57
Ballast, sand, etc.	1·82
All castings	4·13
Lead, sheet and pipes	2·18
Locks, latches, ironmongery, nails, screws, and taps	2·81
Paint, varnish, wall paper, putty, glass, oil, glue, etc	2·38
Gas fittings	0·75
Sundry materials	1·26
Labour of all kinds	35·77
Overhead charges of all kinds, including fees	11·50
Total cost	100·00

CHAPTER VIII

Materials

THE question whether stone, brick, cement, concrete, or wood should be used is one that is generally settled by regard to local conditions. If good brickmaking materials exist in the district, probably there is no better or more adaptable material for artisan's dwellings. Where no brick clay exists but there is good aggregate for cement concrete, this material will be indicated, while in districts where stone is plentiful there are many ways of using this economically.

A good deal has been written recently on the subject of cement concrete as compared with bricks, and it may be said at once that, given satisfactory construction, an exceedingly comfortable dwelling may be built either of blocks of artificial cement stone or of slabs of concrete. The tendency to condensation inside a dwelling-house built of cement concrete can be entirely obviated by hollow walls. By standardising the blocks and by making them on the site it is possible in many instances to build houses of this material at a cheaper rate than those of brickwork.

Housing and Public Health

Brick walls. — It has already been stated that solid-built 9-in. walls are nearly always more or less damp, according to the quality of the bricks and the degree of exposure to wind and rain. A house built with a more or less porous 9-in. wall must always be cold and damp, and it therefore requires at the outset to be rough-cast, or covered on the outside with cement or other material. Such a covering will prevent the damp from striking through, and if, in addition, care is taken to cover the inner surfaces with a not too hard plaster there will be little risk of condensation.

Hollow walls. — Undoubtedly a hollow wall in brickwork, as is pointed out in Chapter II., is better than a similar thickness of solid wall—the cavity being a good non-conductor, and at the same time preventing damp from striking through. For ordinary cottages two 4½-in. walls, properly bound together with ties, are the minimal type of construction which should be considered. This makes an excellent wall, sufficiently strong and well constructed for any ordinary cottage.

There are points, however, which render this type of wall expensive. In the first place, it cannot be built by the bricklayer at the same rate at which he builds a 9-in. wall, because great care has to be taken to prevent mortar from filling the cavity and acting as a conductor of damp; and the tradesmen who follow the bricklayer, such as the

106

Materials

carpenters, have to be careful with their woodwork when closing cavities. On the whole, it is desirable either to provide a hollow wall as described, or to cover the ordinary 9-in. brick wall with an impervious layer. Exact experiments have demonstrated that such a hollow wall is as effectual in protecting against heat transmission as a solid brick wall 18 in. in thickness.

Roofs.—In the absence of sound timber at reasonable cost, it may be necessary to make use of flat roofs. There is now no difficulty in providing a material which will stand both the sun and the weather without disintegrating. Many of the bituminous compounds will go for long periods without any deterioration. Where such a flat roof is provided, a ventilated air space of at least 9 in. should intervene between the roof and the ceiling of the bedroom.

Slate roofs.—There has been a tendency in recent years to cheapen the roof by covering it with the thinnest slates which can be obtained, these being nailed with copper or galvanised iron nails. Much trouble, however, is occasioned by such light roofs being damaged by wind and then leaking. Again, if the galvanised iron nails are damaged they rust through and allow the slates to slip, which necessitates frequent repairs. As a rule, it is better to have fairly strong timbers and thick slates; the first cost will be amply saved by the obviation of repairs which otherwise will be necessary during the first twenty years of the life of the building.

In many areas satisfactory tiles can be obtained, in which case the pitch of the roof will have to be adapted for tiles. The most important points to be attended to in the case of tiles are that they shall be of a quality which will not disintegrate, and of a shape which will prevent rain from being blown underneath.

Asbestos slates have been used to a considerable extent of late years. It is impossible, however, to say as yet how long they will last. In many buildings they have been in use for over twenty years, and it is thought, therefore, that they will be permanent. There is a great advantage in having these light slates, because the rest of the roof may be correspondingly light in structure. The disadvantage is that they allow heat and cold to pass through with great ease.

Internal surfaces.—Everywhere in the house the internal surfaces should be smooth and rendered with plaster, except, perhaps, the coal store and the larder. In the living-room for the artisan's family it is extremely desirable to provide a dado of cement rather than of plaster up to a height of, say, 3 ft. Such a dado will prevent damage to the walls.

Skirting boards, mouldings, etc.—In recent

Materials

years a good deal of unnecessary expense has been incurred in providing deep skirting boards and heavy mouldings. Wherever possible these should be done away with (*see* p. 28), and the smallest possible amount of woodwork should be provided instead of a skirting board.

Floors.—No satisfactory material except wood is available for the flooring of rooms. Wood is probably the best material for every floor except those of the scullery, hall, and passages. A great deal of waste has been incurred from floors being laid with unseasoned timber on rafters over an unventilated cavity. Many of these floors have to be taken up after a few years. It is therefore very important that timber floors on the ground level should have adequate ventilation below them. Such floor boards should be tongued and grooved. For the artisan's living-room, wooden floors are better than any kind of tiles or any kind of cement concrete.

Of late years a large number of flooring compositions have been placed on the market. Few, if any, of them, however, have stood the test of time in any floor which is exposed and on which there is much traffic. Until their durability has been proved it will be well to avoid such materials. Coke breeze concrete, to which linoleum is glued, makes an excellent and sanitary floor if the linoleum is glued upon perfectly dry concrete. If, however, damp rises through the concrete the linoleum will disintegrate in a few years. If a cavity can be ensured below such floors, linoleum glued to dry concrete makes a very comfortable living-room floor.

Windows.—Little more need be said here on the general question of windows (*see* p. 42). (*see* p. 42) There is a tendency in many instances to provide large bay windows in living-rooms. This adds considerably to the size of the room and to its lighting, but unfortunately such a window often makes the room extremely cold and draughty in winter time. The custom of using coloured glass for the upper portions of windows, especially bay windows, should be avoided, because it neutralises the most effective part of the window. Bay windows are frequently costly in upkeep, unless very substantial. On the other hand, they often assist in preventing monotony in the elevation.

The best type of window is not easy to define. Local custom more frequently than anything else decides the type to be used. In some areas sash windows predominate; in others, casements, while in many artisans' dwellings sliding sashes are used. The points to be borne in mind in window construction are: (1) That the lighting area of the window should extend to or near to, the ceiling; (2) that every window should be capable of being opened, and opened in such a way as not

Materials

to allow the admission of rain; (3) that each window should be capable of being easily cleaned. One of the cheapest windows for artisans' dwellings is that in which the frames slide over one another and the upper portion has a top-hung hopper. Such a window is cheap, durable, and efficient for bedrooms.

Plumbing.—A hot-and-cold water supply for a labourer's dwelling must not, in future, be regarded as exceptional. Care must be taken to ensure that a reasonably good quality of plumbing materials is used, and that the waterpipes are properly placed. In designing a cottage considerable care should be bestowed upon the distribution of the hot-and-cold-water pipes, so that from the very beginning there may be little risk of freezing. Similar precautions should be taken in regard to the supply cistern and other parts of the water-supply apparatus.

CHAPTER IX

Communal Services

IT has frequently been urged that a common service of **hot water** should be provided for cottage property. Undoubtedly it would be a real aid to cleanliness, and would be a great means of saving labour. The possibility of such a service is greater in tenement dwellings than in separate cottages. The real difficulty in providing a hot-water service is to prevent the water from being wasted. If some kind of meter could be provided, so that the hot water could be charged for in proportion to the amount used, such a service would be practicable, although even then it would add somewhat to the expense of the cottage.

Central heating. — An artisan's dwelling with good radiators in the living room and parlour, and with a gas stove and a common hot-water supply, is the type of dwelling which reduces the housewife's work to a minimum. If to these were added electricity for lighting and power, an extremely comfortable cottage could be provided.

In regard to central heating, however, what is

Communal Services

easily possible in tenement buildings is almost impracticable in separate cottages on account of the waste through loss of heat from the mains. Objection may be taken to the provision of radiators instead of open fireplaces, but from a medical point of view there is probably very little reason to fear that the absence of the chimney ventilator would seriously interfere with the health of the occupants. It is probable that if dwelling-houses were provided with radiators rather than with fireplaces, those who live in them would soon lose their dislike of these contrivances.

Play-rooms and crèches.—It has been suggested that there is a desire among tenants to have a place in which toddlers and babies may be left in safety while the mothers do their marketing or the heavy work of the house. A crèche for babies would have to be supervised by a skilled person, and the premises themselves must be of good class. The expense of running a crèche for babies must, therefore, be high. Such a scheme, indeed, however desirable, is almost doomed to failure by its expensiveness. So far as toddlers are concerned, however, the provision of a small open space near the dwelling, where they can play together, under supervision, need not be very costly.

Communal clothes washing.—Many inquiries have been made as to how the inconvenience and

Housing and Public Health

drudgery of washing and drying clothes in a small house can be avoided. Common washhouses have long been in existence in many towns. To these washhouses a mother may take her washing, and either do it herself completely, or do certain parts, reserving the finishing to be done at home. Such a washing establishment away from home means, of course, that the mother must either take her children with her or leave them with a neighbour or at a crèche.

The really hard part of the weekly washing is the soaking, scrubbing, and boiling of the clothes. It has therefore been suggested that arrangements might be made to send all the heavy articles of clothing to an ordinary laundry, where they could be washed and rough-dried, leaving the ironing, etc., to be done by the housewife at home. This is probably a good suggestion, and in time it may be carried out.

Even at pre-war prices it would almost certainly not be economical for the artisan classes to send their clothes to a laundry to be washed and finished. It is estimated that the washing of the clothes of an ordinary family of six — father, mother, and four children — would cost, for materials, about 8d. per week if done at home, while if sent to an ordinary laundry it would cost at least 6s.

Vacuum cleaning.—If it were possible to find

Communal Services

a common heating and hot-water supply, or to provide a cheap electric lighting installation, it would be possible also to provide mechanical power for driving a vacuum cleaner on each floor, and thus save labour in cleaning. At present, however, all these labour-saving apparatus are costly and out of the question, as is also the provision of electric power.

CHAPTER X

Rural Cottages

THERE is not much difficulty in arriving at the minimal requirements of a rural labourer's cottage, judged from the point of view of health. No body of men has such opportunities as the medical profession for seeing the rural labourer's dwelling "at work," and of learning from the people themselves what they need. I can say with considerable definiteness that the absence of reasonable accommodation for agricultural labourers has largely been the cause of the migration from the country to town. Not only is there a great shortage of dwelling-houses in many rural areas, but many of the existing houses are insanitary, or defective in accommodation.

The first and most important requirement for the country is more houses, which should be provided before any attempt is made to deal with existing insanitary ones. The sites for new houses are limited to places where work is available, and therefore a large number of these houses must be scattered. While this is so, it is important to

Rural Cottages

remember that labourers prefer to live in a hamlet and travel to their work on foot or on a bicycle rather than live in an isolated house.

So far as the lay-out of these houses is con-

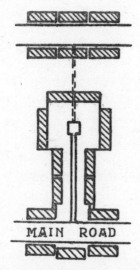

Fig. 11.—To show method of siting houses away from main road.
(*From the Report of the Tudor Walters Committee.*)

cerned, there is no material difference between them and new houses in an urban district. One would urge the undesirability of building on main roads, which are always disagreeable on account of the amount of dust and the danger to young children from traffic. Houses should therefore

Housing and Public Health

be built well back from the road, and, if necessary, on separate little culs-de-sac, as shown in the accompanying plan (Fig. 11).

Size of the cottage.—There is no essential difference in the requirements of the rural labourer's family compared with those of the town dweller. More often than in towns the parlour is dispensed with (Fig. 12), but there are the same reasons in the country as in the town for the

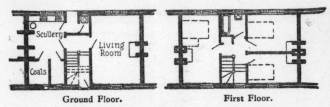

Ground Floor.   First Floor.

Fig. 12.—Cottage without parlour, suitable in some rural areas.

(From the Report of the Tudor Walters Committee.)

provision of a parlour. The house should have three bedrooms. A parlour and an extra bedroom are extremely useful to rural labourers with large families, or for the accommodation of lodgers, who are a source of income, and must be provided for in one way or another. The Report of the Committee of the Board of Agriculture and Fisheries on plans for rural cottages gives the following dimensions for rooms in a house with a parlour:

118

Rural Cottages

					Floor space in sq. ft.
Parlour (if provided)	.	.	.	.	120
Living-room	.	.	.	.	180
Scullery .	.	.	.	.	80
Larder .	.	.	.	.	24
Bedroom No. 1	.	.	.	.	160
Bedroom No. 2	.	.	.	.	120
Bedroom No. 3	.	.	.	.	110

Scullery and bathroom.—Where a constant water supply is available there ought to be no hesitation in providing an upstairs bathroom. Where, however, such a supply is not available, then one of the makeshift bathing arrangements will have to be provided. In this case the scullery might have a fixed bath in it, or it might have a tip-up bath, the water being obtained from a washing boiler placed near. In such a cottage it is undesirable to have the bathroom upstairs because of the labour of carrying up water. There will therefore be no necessity for providing a heating boiler behind the kitchen range.

Water-closet accommodation. — The rural labourer has until very recent years had to be content with an open midden privy situated frequently at a long distance from the house. Illness has arisen from these privies; they are usually most offensive and disgusting, and should not be tolerated.

There are in the market many varieties of earth

closets. The simpler these closets are in their mechanism the better. Perhaps the best arrangement is to build a closet and provide an ordinary coal bucket under a lift-up seat. At the back of the seat is a large open box for earth, with a scoop. If a shovelful of earth is placed in the closet every time it is used there ought to be no liquid obvious, and no smell from the bucket. If the handle of the bucket is taken off and hung on the wall it can be hooked on to the bucket when it is full, and the whole may then be carried at frequent intervals to a trench in the garden and emptied.

The floor of such a closet should be made of cement concrete, and should be smooth, so that it may be swilled out at intervals. This form of closet is simple in construction, and if used with quite ordinary care is a quite sanitary apparatus. It may, indeed, be placed under the main roof of the building, but without an opening to the inside.

Water supply.—As already stated (p. 46), the main feature to be secured is that the water supply, if from a well, shall be free from the risk of pollution. The well should therefore be some distance from the house. In the rural labourer's scullery there should be a shelf on which buckets of water may be stored.

Drainage and disposal of liquid refuse.—The late Dr. Vivian Poore demonstrated on a large

Rural Cottages

scale that the whole of the drainage from a labourer's cottage may be profitably and safely disposed of in a small garden. There is no doubt about this being practicable, but without considerable education and supervision such a system is liable to get out of order and become a nuisance.

It therefore becomes a necessity to provide a cesspool or to instal some general sewage disposal system. It is a good plan to separate the water which comes from the roof and the yard from slop waters, and to allow the former to soak into the ground or to be retained for washing purposes, while the sink water is run into a cesspool. If the cesspool is situated at a sufficient distance from the well there is no reason why it should not be pervious and, therefore, self-cleansing. This is preferable to the water-tight cesspool suggested by the Local Government Board, which has the disadvantage of requiring to be pumped out at frequent intervals, and of suggesting to the tenant the desirability of using as little water as possible so as to avoid nuisance and save labour.

Tool houses and fuel stores.—These are very valuable additions to the rural labourer's cottage. They ought to be large enough to enable him to store his winter wood or coal, and to keep all the tools he requires for his work.

Materials for the country cottage.—It is a great mistake to import materials into a district

Housing and Public Health

when reasonably good building stone or bricks can be obtained on the spot. To a much larger extent, therefore, in rural than in urban areas, is it necessary to seek out what is available in the district.

Another point of importance is that the rural builder is able to build certain types of houses because he is accustomed to them, while in many cases he is so unfamiliar with other types that the cost of building would be materially enhanced. It is well, therefore, to adapt the style of building to the class of workmanship available in the area.

CHAPTER XI

Housing in London

It has already been mentioned that housing conditions in the capital of nearly every country differ in some respects from those in the provincial towns. A short chapter must, therefore, be devoted to the question of housing in London.

At the same time, a study of the problem as it affects London will furnish hints for provincial towns, because what has happened in London might happen, and indeed is happening, more or less, in many of the largest provincial towns, where people in the central areas are being locked in by enormous suburban areas, preventing them from getting into the country without a long journey. If London could have known in Wren's time that the city would grow until it extended fifteen miles from the centre, care would have been taken to provide special means of transit, and otherwise to facilitate the distribution of the people in the outer areas.

But London has been much more fortunate than most of our provincial towns in having parks of large size in and around it. There is scarcely one of our provincial towns with an open space of the size of Hyde Park in its central area.

The impossibility, even now, of regulating the growth of London is indicated by the fact that the County of London has, not reckoning the City of London proper, no less than twenty-eight authorities with certain housing functions to fulfil. But these authorities deal with only a small portion of the population living within a radius of 15 miles from Charing Cross. In the outer ring there is a very large number of local authorities, all invested with housing responsibilities. These, added to the authorities in the County of London, give a total of eighty-eight. With so many authorities, it is impossible to secure anything like uniform action and vigour. Similar conditions also occur in many of the largest provincial towns in the country.

A central authority needed. — The first and most essential step in the direction of housing in an area like London is to set up some central authority to regulate the provision of houses throughout the whole area. Such an authority, in addition to controlling the provision of houses, would at the same time deal with the provision of means of transit. By moving out the people and cheapening the cost of travel, the housing difficulty in London might be very con-

Housing in London

siderably relieved, but it is evident that in an area so enormous in extent large numbers of people must be provided for in the more or less central parts. There appears to be no alternative but to provide tenement dwellings for those who have to live in these central parts, and if such tenement dwellings are built they ought to be self-contained, and to have sufficient airing ground to mitigate as far as practicable the evils of the tenement system.

Many such housing schemes have already been carried out by the Peabody Trust, the County Council and various other local authorities, apparently with very good results. It cannot, however, be too frequently stated that up to the present time most of these results have been obtained from dwellers who are unconsciously selected.

In London, as elsewhere, much attention has been lately given to the reparation of old properties and the division of middle-class houses into sections for the artisan classes. The former subject is considered in the next chapter. The adaptation of middle-class houses to the requirements of artisans is a device that may be commended, since it tends to spread the artisan population over larger areas.

CHAPTER XII

The Reparation of Old Properties

A GREAT deal can be done, and must be done, in the way of reparation of old dwellings during the period which must elapse before a sufficiency of healthy new dwellings is provided. In many of these cases of reparation the standards to be aimed at must fall much below those which have been outlined as being needed for new dwellings. It is possible, however, to make many old houses very much more healthy than they are at present by carrying out substantial repairs.

Obligations on landlords.—It cannot be too widely known that the owner of a small house who lets it at a rental up to £40 per annum in London, up to £26 per annum in a town of 50,000 inhabitants, or up to £16 per annum elsewhere, does so with an implied contract that the house is reasonably fit for human habitation.

By Section 15 of the Housing, Town Planning, etc., Act, 1909, the group of houses mentioned in the above paragraph must be kept by the owner during the holding "in all respects reasonably fit

Reparation

for human habitation." That is to say, a tenant who finds that a landlord has let him a cottage which is not reasonably fit for human habitation, or does not continue to keep it in that condition, has a remedy at common law. Innumerable cases have been taken into Court under this section.

Further, if it appears to the sanitary authority that a house is not kept "in all respects reasonably fit for human habitation," the sanitary authority must cause a written notice to be sent to the landlord requiring him within a reasonable time (not being less than twenty-one days) to do such work, specified in the notice, as is necessary to make the dwelling habitable. If he fails, power is given to the sanitary authority to do the work and recover the expense.

Nothing could be more definite and satisfactory than the powers contained in these two sections. If the tenant suffers without complaining it is due to ignorance of his rights, or to neglect to avail himself of them. Probably much more might be done by sanitary authorities in making the occupants of small dwelling-house property aware of the protection which these sections afford. So, too, it is desirable that sanitary authorities should take a much more serious view of the duty devolving upon them of requiring landlords to keep their houses in a habitable condition.

Housing and Public Health

Regular inspection of dwellings.—Section 17 (1) of the Housing, Town Planning, etc., Act, 1909, requires that every local authority shall cause a regular inspection of the houses in its district to be made, with a view to ascertaining what houses are dangerous or injurious to health. Regulations have been made by the Local Government Board, known as the Housing (Inspection of District) Regulations, 1910, requiring the Medical Officer of Health of every district to organise an examination of dwelling-houses in relation to the following matters :

1. The arrangements for preventing contamination of the water supply.
2. Water-closet accommodation.
3. Drainage.
4. The condition of the dwelling-house in regard to light, the free circulation of air, dampness, and cleanliness.
5. The paving, drainage, and sanitary condition of any yard or outhouses belonging to or occupied with the dwelling-house.
6. The arrangements for the deposit of refuse and ashes.
7. The existence of any room which, in pursuance of sub-section (7) of Section 17 of the Act of 1909, would be a dwelling-house so dangerous or injurious to health as to be unfit for human habitation.

Reparation

8. Any defects in other matters which may tend to render the dwelling-house dangerous or injurious to the health of an inhabitant.

It is obvious from the above that if a sanitary authority carries out its duties it is possible for it to know of every house which is dangerous or injurious to health, and every house that requires ordinary repairs. The importance of this statutory inspection cannot be over-estimated.

Powers of the sanitary authorities.—Having ascertained that certain houses are dangerous or injurious to health, the sanitary authority has drastic powers for dealing with them, which will now be enumerated.

(*a*) *Closing order.*—Section 17 of the Housing, Town Planning, etc., Act, 1909, empowers a sanitary authority, if a house is reported by the Medical Officer of Health as dangerous or injurious to health, to require it to be closed when it has satisfied itself that the report is justified. In such a case, indeed, it has no alternative but to make a closing order, prohibiting the house from being used for human habitation "until, in the judgment of the local authority, the dwelling is rendered fit for the purpose."

(*b*) *Demolition order.*—Obviously one of two things must be done by the owner. He may put

J   129

Housing and Public Health

is an unhealthy area, and forthwith to make a scheme for improving it.

The details to be taken into consideration in making a scheme under this part of the Act are complicated, and are subject to the approval of the Local Government Board, by means of a local inquiry at which all interests can be represented. In practice the method of procedure under this part of the Act has been found to be exceedingly costly, slow, and unsatisfactory. In many cases it is necessary to clear the site, and for this purpose to purchase, it may be by arbitration, the whole of the land, dwelling-houses, shops, public-houses, workshops, factories, etc., together with the business interests involved. When this has been done, new streets may have to be formed, and new buildings erected on the land by private enterprise or by the local authority. It is usually found that, by the time all this has been done, the land is so expensive as to be quite unsuitable for the erection of cottage property. In a few special cases the procedure has been satisfactory; but in the great majority of towns one experience of the full operation of this part of the Act has been sufficient to make the local authority exceedingly reluctant to undertake a second scheme. On the whole, the cost of purchasing old slums has prevented large areas of town dwellings from being dealt with under this clause.

Reparation

In the future, work under this part of the Act is likely to be so expensive as to be prohibitive. What, then, can be done in such circumstances? The answer is: First, obtain powers to town-plan the area, and then put into operation the existing powers as to closing or reparation or demolition.

At present, however, there is no power to town-plan an old built-up area. This is regrettable, as it prevents the local authority from deciding which of the old areas can be scheduled as residential. Whenever such an area is demarcated for residences, it is possible to apply all those conditions to it which have already been described and which have for their object the making of the area a pleasant one to live in. It will pay to spend money on parks and play spaces, and in beautifying the area, if it is known that it will remain mainly a residential area and not be used for factory or business purposes.

CHAPTER XIII

Building of Houses in New Areas

PART III. of the Act of 1890 gives large powers for the acquisition of land by local authorities, and for the erection of houses on such land. As the dwellings which are needed to meet the present acute shortage will be erected under these powers, it is desirable to understand the procedure which must be adopted.

Definitions.—In the first place the Housing Act of 1890 makes use of the expression "lodging houses for the working classes" instead of "houses" or "cottages." The expression "lodging house" is an unfortunate relic of preceding Acts of Parliament, which have long since been superseded. There were several Acts passed between 1851 and 1885 dealing with "labouring classes' lodging houses." In recent years the expression "lodging houses" has come to be applied to a type of property entirely different from that contemplated by the Acts of Parliament relating to housing.

By Section 53 of the Act of 1890 the expression

Houses in New Areas

"lodging house" is defined to include separate houses for the working classes, and the expression "cottage" may include a garden of not more than half an acre, provided the estimated annual value of such garden shall not exceed £3.

Again, Section 59 permits the local authority to "fit up, furnish, and supply the same respectively with all requisite furniture, fittings, and conveniences." The local authority may also make byelaws for the management, use, and regulation of "lodging houses," a printed copy or abstract of such to be put up and at all times kept in every room.

It is obvious, therefore, that lodgings were originally intended. There can, however, be no doubt as to the intention of the legislature in the Housing and Town Planning Bill of 1919, viz. that ordinary houses or cottages shall be erected, whatever expression may be used to define them.

Another important point, and one which is not very clear in any of the Acts of Parliament, is as to the classes of the community a local authority must provide houses for. In numerous Acts of Parliament the expression "working classes" is made use of. By paragraph 12 of the Schedule to the Housing Act of 1903 the expression "working classes" is defined as including "mechanics, artisans, labourers, and others working for wages, hawkers, costermongers, persons not working for

Housing and Public Health

wages but working at some trade or handicraft without employing others except members of their own family, and persons other than domestic servants whose income, in any case, does not exceed an average of thirty shillings per week, and the families of any such persons who may be residing with them."

In the Settled Land Act, which is referred to in the Housing Act of 1890, the provisions "apply only to buildings of a rateable value not exceeding £100 per annum."

By Section 75 of the Act of 1890, "letting for habitation by persons of the working classes" means "letting for habitation of a house or part of a house at a rent not exceeding in England the sum named as the limit for the composition of the rates by Section 3 of the Poor Rate Assessment and Collection Act, 1869, and in Scotland and Ireland the sum of £4."

The Act of 1909 again extends the definition. Here Section 14 deals with the question of houses with rentals up to £40 per annum in London, £26 per annum in towns of 50,000 inhabitants or over, and £16 per annum elsewhere, so as to bring them within the scope of the special legislation relating to small dwellings.

The above definitions have been set out to indicate the extreme amount of confusion and want of directness which exists in our legislation as to the classes of the community for which compulsory powers in regard to housing are given to local authorities. The plans and instruction which have been recently issued by the Local Government Board indicate that what the Government is prepared to sanction at present is a good class artisan's dwelling and nothing more. This is unfortunate, because there are few large estates which could not be improved vastly by the erection of houses for the middle and upper classes in parts of it, thus preventing the aggregation together of masses of the labouring classes. It seems desirable, therefore, that at an early date all references to the working classes should be left out, so that, when building, local authorities may provide for the mixing of the classes in the areas which they control.

Purchase of land by a local authority.—The local authority, with the consent of the Local Government Board, may purchase land for housing by agreement, notwithstanding that the land is not immediately required for this purpose.

Land may also be purchased compulsorily by the local authority for housing. In this case it must be done by means of an Order which will require confirmation by the Local Government Board or Parliament.

In selecting the locality for a housing scheme,

137

Housing and Public Health

the Act requires that consideration shall be
given to :

(a) The probable growth of the district.
(b) Its accessibility to industrial, social, edu-
cational, and recreational centres.
(c) Transit facilities.
(d) Suitability of land for healthy dwellings,
with reasonable amenity.
(e) Its cost and the quality of the soil.

The site having been selected and the purchase
completed, the lay out of the land must be undertaken.   This is best done by a combination of
architectural, surveying, and economic skill.   The
total cost of a completed housing scheme under
Part III. of the Act of 1890 must include surveyor's
and legal expenses, the cost of formation of roads,
fencing, planting, drainage, and sewerage, as well
as the costs in connection with the erection of the
dwellings.

Borrowing by a local authority.—The Act
of 1890 empowers a local authority to defray the
expenses of a housing scheme as part of the general
expenses of the Public Health Act of 1875, and,
further, empowers the local authority to borrow for
the purpose for a period which may not in any case
be more than eighty years.   A local authority may
sell or exchange land for housing purposes (Act
of 1890, Section 60).

Houses in New Areas

By the Act of 1903 a local authority may provide and maintain, in connection with the housing scheme, recreation grounds, shops, or other buildings which will serve a beneficial purpose in connection with the requirements of the persons for whom the scheme is provided.

The Act of 1900 provides for the leasing of any land required for housing to a lessee for the purpose of erecting and maintaining houses, and requires that the local authority shall insert in every such lease provisions which will secure the user of the land and buildings for the classes mentioned in the Housing Acts.

Private Utility Societies may, under the Act of 1890, borrow money from the Public Loan Commissioners, such societies to include "any railway company or dock or harbour company or any other company, society, or association established for the purpose of constructing or improving or facilitating or encouraging the construction or improvement of dwelling houses for the working classes or for trading or manufacturing purposes."

Similarly, money may be borrowed by any private individual entitled to any land for an estate in fee simple or for a term of years absolute, whereof not less than fifty years shall remain unexpired. It is proposed to extend this power by the Housing and Town Planning Bill of 1919.

Housing and Public Health

Unnecessary complications of the law relating to housing.—It must be obvious to anyone perusing these brief references to housing legislation that the time is opportune for a consolidating and simplifying Act to which one could turn for all information in regard to the housing question. At the present time we have to deal with five or six Acts of Parliament, each succeeding Act amending the former one, so that the earliest and most important of all the Acts, viz. the 'Act of 1890, has been so amended that it would be a dangerous procedure for anyone to be guided by it alone. Few of the sections in it are now operative in their original form.

CHAPTER XIV

The Present Shortage and the Proposed Remedy

THROUGHOUT Great Britain there has been during the past ten years a diminishing number of new houses erected annually. Since the commencement of the War practically no new dwellings have been erected. The shortage of new houses has varied in different towns, but no town has escaped altogether. In few rural districts have any houses been erected during these years; yet during the whole of the time the population has been increasing at its average pace. As illustrating the acuteness of the position, it is estimated that there is a shortage of 12,000 houses in Birmingham.

In examining this question one has always to bear in mind that the average number of empty houses in any district in normal times varies from 5 to 10 per cent. In Birmingham it varied from 8 to 9 per cent. for a long period of years. This percentage of empty houses is a matter of great importance to the community, for without it it would be almost impossible to remove to another house

Housing and Public Health

either because the existing one was unsuitable or because the existing one required such substantial repair as to entail removal of the tenant. Even before the War the whole of these void houses were occupied from time to time, except, perhaps, a few which were uninhabitable.

It is not easy to explain the slackening in the building of houses before the War. The Royal Commission on Housing in Scotland went into this matter very carefully, and while admitting that it existed and that it was probably due to fear of the imposition of new taxes on property, they stated that in their opinion there was no real reason for such a feeling of insecurity.

With the ever-increasing population empty houses were soon tenanted, and then followed the objectionable crowding of two families into one house. In a certain number of cases this crowding has produced nothing more than inconvenience; but there remains a very large number of cases in which health and decency and comfort are outraged by such overcrowding. Few who have an intimate knowledge of life in a cottage can possibly realise what is meant by two large families attempting to live in one small house. Try, for instance, to accommodate the twenty-one members of two families; that is, two fathers, two mothers, thirteen sons and daughters between 12 and 25 years of age, and four others under 12, in a cottage with

Shortage and Remedy

two bedrooms of moderate size and one bedroom of small size. This is probably an unusual case, but there are thousands nearly as bad.

An investigation was recently made in Birmingham into the conditions under which discharged tuberculous soldiers have been housed since their return from the War. Out of a total of 1,300 consumptive soldiers 600 were visited, and it was found that among these 600 no less than 107 were living in houses containing two families. The explanation offered in most cases was that the soldier's family gave up their house when he left for the War and took cheaper lodgings in another house. When the soldier returned he found that another house could not be found, and he had to live and sleep in his infective condition in the same room as his wife and other members of the family.

Similarly, great inconvenience occurs in such a house when a death takes place. One of the bedrooms has to be reserved for the corpse, and the other members of the family have to crowd into the remaining portion of the house.

Again, the occurrence of serious illness in such a house produces conditions which are inimical to the recovery of the sick person and often intolerable to the other members of the household.

No wonder, then, that of all the questions of the day the one which is felt most keenly and which must be handled in the most drastic manner is that of making up the deficiency of houses in the first instance, and later on grappling with the question of dealing with the slum properties.

Two lines of action have been taken by the Government. In the first place, the Local Government Board,* by their letter of February 6, 1919, have offered substantial assistance to local authorities for building houses. The more important paragraphs are the following :

" The Housing Schemes of local authorities to which the State will be prepared to grant financial assistance, if they are submitted to the Local Government Board within twelve months from this date and carried out within a period of two years from this date, or within such further period as may be approved by the Local Government Board, are :

" Schemes carried out by local authorities under Part III. of the Housing of the Working Classes Act, 1890, for any area for which the Local Government Board are satisfied that it is desirable that houses for the working classes should be provided.

" Rehousing schemes in connection with Improvement and Reconstruction schemes under Parts I. and II. of the Housing of the Working Classes Act, 1890, except that no part of the cost of acquiring and clearing a site would be made the subject of financial assistance if either (a) the site had been acquired or cleared before the date of this letter, or (b) the needs of the district could, in the opinion of the Local Government Board, be adequately met by means of a scheme under Part III.

* Now merged in the Ministry of Health.

Shortage and Remedy

" The full cost of a scheme will in the first instance
be met out of a loan or loans raised by the Local
Authority, and it is particularly desired by the Treasury
that authorities should raise such loans in the open
market wherever it is possible for them to do so. As the
financial assistance to be granted from public funds for
housing schemes will take the form of a subsidy as ex-
plained below, and as it is important to secure that the
whole of the State assistance may be given under one
head, any loans granted from the Local Loans Fund for
the purpose of assisted schemes will not be made at the
preferential rates ordinarily allowed for housing loans,
but at a rate fixed by the Treasury so as to correspond
with the full current market rate of interest.

" In respect of any housing scheme or series of housing schemes carried out by a local authority within the
period referred to above, Parliament will be asked to
vote financial assistance calculated on a basis estimated
to relieve the local authority of the burden of any annual
deficit in so far as it exceeds the products of a rate of a
penny in the pound on the area chargeable, but there
will be no contribution towards the cost where the annual
excess of expenditure over income would not exceed that
amount."

  .   .   &#x1F;   &#x1F;   .   .

" When the houses have been built and let, the
amount of the subsidy to be paid thereafter during a
transitional period ending 31st March, 1927, will be
settled on a basis of a revised balance sheet showing the
actual expenditure incurred and the *actual* rents obtained.
The interest charged on loans will be taken at the
amounts actually to be paid if the loans are raised from
the Local Loans Fund or other outside sources. Where
the money is provided from accumulated funds in the
hands of the local authority interest will be calculated

Housing and Public Health

at the rate in force for loans for assisted housing schemes from the Local Loans Fund (unless the local authority is also borrowing from other outside sources in respect of its scheme, in which case interest should be charged on advances from accumulated funds at the rate paid for the loans from such other outside sources). Where there is found to be a deficit in excess of the produce of a rate of a penny in the pound, the rate of annual contribution so determined will hold good for the remainder of the transitional period."

.   .   .   .   .   .

"At the end of the transitional period the whole position will be reviewed in the light of the actual working of the scheme during that period, and the annual amount thereafter to be provided out of public funds will be adjusted as follows: The amount of the estimated annual expenditure will be compared anew with the amount of the estimated annual income, and if as a result of this comparison it appears that the future annual charges to be borne by the local authority are likely to exceed the produce of a rate of a penny in the pound, the annual subsidy for the remainder of the period of the loan will be finally fixed at a sum calculated to cover this excess, subject only to such adjustment as may be required in consequence of any variation in the amount produced by a penny rate.

"At the final adjustment it will be open to the Local Government Board to reduce the amount of the State contribution if there has been evidence of failure on the part of the local authority to exercise due economy in management, or in securing the best rents obtainable. In the event of the local authority and the Local Government Board being unable to reach an agreement on any such question the matter will be referred for final settlement to some independent tribunal."

Shortage and Remedy

The second line of action of the Government is to bring in further legislation, in the form of the Housing and Town Planning Bill, 1919, with a view to improving and facilitating the powers of the local authority for building new houses to meet the extraordinary needs of the time.

Clauses 1 to 6 of this Bill impose on the local authority the duty of considering the needs of its district in regard to the building of new houses under Part III. of the Housing Act of 1890, and of submitting within three months, and thereafter as often as occasion arises, a scheme setting out the number and nature of the houses to be provided, the time within which such scheme can be carried out, and other similar particulars. Where a local authority fails in this duty the Local Government Board may require the County Council to prepare and carry out a scheme, or they may themselves do so at the cost of the local authority.

Further, where the Local Government Board are satisfied that the scheme is necessary under Part I. or Part II. of the Act of 1890 in dealing with old house property, they may require the local authority, by order, to carry out such a scheme "irrespective of the sufficiency or otherwise of their resources."

Clause 7 of the Bill provides for financial assistance, and the wording is such as already to have given rise to much discussion as to its exact meaning. In simple language, the clause provides for recouping a local authority a part of any loss which may be incurred in building houses under the new Bill or under Part I. or Part II. of the Act of 1890. The Government have only undertaken to recoup the loss if the building or reconstruction is done within a time to be specified by the Local Government Board and Treasury, the amount of the annual payment to be determined on the basis of the estimated annual loss subject to the deduction of an amount equal to the produce of a rate of one penny in the pound levied in the area. That is to say, during the War emergency the whole of the loss over and above the amount raised by a penny rate will be borne by the National Exchequer.

The Bill proposes to give to local authorities much wider powers for dealing with Public Utility Societies, and it gives to these societies greater facilities for obtaining the necessary capital to erect dwellings. A Public Utility Society is defined as one "registered under the Industrial and Provident Societies Act, 1893, or any amendment thereof, the rules whereof prohibit the payment of any interest or dividend at a rate exceeding 6 per cent. per annum."

Facilities for private individuals.—The Bill provides for the granting of loans by the Public Works Loan Commissioners to private individuals

Shortage and Remedy

for the purpose of constructing houses for the working classes, such loans to be granted on the security of a mortgage up to 75 per cent. of the value, provided the houses are constructed in accordance with plans approved by the Local Government Board.

It may be said, therefore, that the whole object of the Housing and Town Planning Bill of 1919 is to cause a rapid provision of a large number of houses of a character far superior to the majority of houses now occupied by the working classes. The type, however, is by no means too good; it corresponds very closely to the recommendations and opinions expressed in the earlier chapters of this book.

The annual rental for these new houses is likely to be considerably more than the working classes in the past have been accustomed to pay. A house which formerly cost £250 to erect will now cost probably something approaching £700, and it is likely, therefore, that rentals will be at least double what they were in pre-War days.

On the whole, the outlook for a satisfactory solution of the great task which is now before the nation is distinctly hopeful. Parliament and the local authorities have already made a material advance in the direction of solving the problem. Bricks, wood, slates, and fittings will be turned out in large quantities as the result of Government

Housing and Public Health

action in guaranteeing prices. It now remains for every local authority and for every manufacturer employing large numbers of workpeople to take up the work with energy and persistence. If this be done, there is little doubt that the housing of the people will, in a very few years, be put on a plane of excellence which it has never reached before.

SOME STANDARD WORKS
OF REFERENCE

LAW

Allen, " Housing of the Working Classes "

Publishers

Butterworth &
Co.

HOUSING

Thompson, " Housing Handbook " . P. S. King & Co.

Nettlefold, " Practical Housing " . . Fisher Unwin.

R. Eberstadt, "Handbuch des Wohnungs-
wesens " . . . . . Fischer, Jena.

P. Alden, " Housing " . . . . Headley Bros.

TOWN PLANS

Aldridge, " The Case for Town Planning "

National Housing
Council.

Horsfall, " The Example of Germany "

Manchester Uni-
versity Press

Inigo Twigg, " Town Planning " . . Methuen.

G. Cadbury, jun., " Town Planning " . Longmans, Green
& Co.

Sennett, " Garden Cities " . . Bemrose.

OFFICIAL PUBLICATIONS

Report on the Royal Commission on
Housing for Scotland. Cd. 8731 . H.M. Stationery
Office.

Works of Reference

INDEX

Index

Index

FENCE for cottage gardens, better than walls, 89

Flies, and household refuse, 57

Floor space, in barracks, standard of, 33

Floors, damp, 27; smoothness of, 28; wood best material for, 109

Footpaths, width of, 83; construction of, 84

Four-roomed houses, mortality-rate in, 13

Fuel stores, for rural cottages, 121

GARDEN space, economics of, 80

Glasgow, tenement buildings in, 12

Grit stone, as building material, 26

Gully traps, 88

HALL, in artisans' dwelling, 94

Hampstead Garden Suburb, number of houses per acre in, 75

Health, influence of environment on, 9; influence of bad housing on, 12

Heating, communal, 112

Hill, Prof. Leonard, Report of, on Ventilation, 32

Hitzslag, and deaths from heat-stroke, 24

Hot-and-cold water supply for artisans' dwellings, 111

Hot-water service, communal, 112

House, artisan's, parlour of, 90; scullery of, 91; size of living-room and parlour in, 92; hall and stairs of, 94; washhouse of, 94; water-closet accommodation of, 97; larder of, 98; coal store of, 99;

bathroom of, 99; bedrooms of, 99; attic rooms in, 100; cupboards and shelves in, 101; cost of, 101; economies in building of, 102; percentage cost of, 103. (*See also* Cottage, rural)

Housework, facilities for lessening, 49

Houses, old, reparation of, 126

—— per acre, number of, in town-planning schemes, 73; and size of, 79

—— shortage of, 141; and consequent overcrowding, 143; Government action to remedy, 144

—— unfit for habitation, powers and duties of sanitary authorities as to, 127, 129

Housing and Town-planning Act (1909), 126, 127, 129

—— —— —— Bill (1919), 135, 139, 147; object of, 149

—— bad, a component of a vicious circle, 6

—— need for simplification of law as to, 140

—— of Working Classes Act (1890), provisions of as to unfit dwellings, 130

—— Regulations (1910), and inspection of dwellings, 128

—— rural, deficiency of, a main cause of migration to towns, 116

—— schemes, powers of local authorities as to, 134; offer of Government assistance for, 144; and Housing and Town-planning Bill (1919), 147

Index

Index

Index

127, 129; inspection of houses by, 128; powers of, as to unhealthy areas, 131. (*See also* Local authorities.)

Sanitary fittings, 54

Scullery, in artisan's dwelling, desirability of separate, 91; size and uses of, 92
—— in rural cottages, 119

Self-contained houses, definition of, 52; advantages of, 53

Set-back of dwellings, in town planning, 77

Shelves, in artisan's dwelling, 101

Site, importance of dryness of, 62

Sites, hilly, and shape of house, 78

Size of houses, and number per acre, 79

Skirting boards, needlessness of, 108

Slates, for roofs, 107; asbestos, 108

Slop closets, 56

Slum-dwellers, responsiveness of, to improved conditions, 10

Slums, death-rates in, 4; in Birmingham, 14; in Liverpool, 14; in Manchester, 15; in London, 15; in Aberdeen, 16; estimated annual loss of life in, in London and county boroughs, 16

Soot in air, harmfulness of, 60

Southwark, overcrowding in, 36

Space around dwellings, importance of, 51; bye-law requirements as to, 52

Spray infection, overcrowding and, 33

Stairs, in artisan's dwelling, 94

Structural requirements of healthy dwelling, 19

Subsidy, Government, for housing schemes, 144

Sunlight, effect of, on germs, 41; obstruction of, by buildings, in winter compared with summer, 78

Surface pollution, and generation of germs, 58

TEMPERATURE, protection against extremes of, in dwellings, 23

Tenement dwellings, unhealthiness of, 66; necessity for, in central parts of London, 125

Three-roomed houses, mortality-rate in, 13

Tiles, for kitchen floors, and dampness, 25, 27; for roofs, 108

Tool houses, for rural cottages, 121

Town Planning Act (1909), essential section of, 67
—— —— Bill (1919), 135, 139, 147, 149
—— —— importance of, 5; separation of manufacturing from residential areas in, 68; provision for amenities in, 69, 72; provision of means of transit in, 69; different kinds of roads in, 71; and number of dwellings per acre, 73; Birmingham schemes of, 74; layout in, 75; mixing classes in, 75; details of, 76; curved roads in, 77; set-back of dwellings in, 77; absence of powers for, in old built-up areas, 133

Trade nuisances, avoidance of, in town planning, 63

158

Index

Transit facilities, provision of, in town planning, 61

Traps, interception, 85; gully, 88

Two-roomed houses, mortality-rate in, 12

UNHEALTHY areas, powers of sanitary authority as to, 131

VACUUM cleaning, 114

Ventilation, 32; from chimney, 38; special devices for, 38; simple test of, 39; of back-to-back houses, 39

Ventilator in pantry or scullery, desirability of, in small houses, 32

WAGES, and house rent, 7

Walls, thickness of, and dampness, 26; smoothness of, 28; plastering of, 30; hollow, 106; impervious covering for, 107

Washhouses, need for, 59; use of scullery as, 97

Washing of clothes, communal, 113

Waste pipes, trapping of, 87

Water-carriage system, in Birmingham, and typhoid fever, 11

Water-closet, in artisans' dwellings, 97; upstairs position of, 98; in rural cottages, 119

Water-closets, used in common, 53, 54, 55

Water supply, inside, necessity for, 44; no legal requirement of, 45

—— —— source of, 46; quantity of per dwelling, in town and country, 46; of rural cottages, 120

Weather, protection from, in dwellings, 21

Winders, 94

Windows, aspect of, 40; dirty, 42; needless screening of, by curtains, 43; bay, pros and cons of, 110; points in construction of, 110; cheap type of, 111

Window-size, deficient, 42; bye-law requirements as to, in new houses, 42

Wood, best material for floors, etc., 109

Woodwork, smoothness of, 28

YARD surfaces, 88

159

PRINTED BY
CASSELL & COMPANY, LIMITED, LA BELLE SAUVAGE,
LONDON, E.C.4
F.20.719